D0965589

Christina Geßner

Long Term Evolution

A concise introduction to
LTE and its measurement requirements

© Rohde & Schwarz GmbH & Co. KG 2011
Mühldorfstraße 15
81671 München
Germany
www.rohde-schwarz.com

Second Edition 2011
Printed in Germany

ISBN 978-3-939837-11-4
PW 0002.8215.00

Table of contents

1 Motivation for introducing LTE

In December 2004, a study item on evolved universal terrestrial radio access (E-UTRA) and the evolved universal terrestrial radio access network (E-UTRAN) was launched within the 3rd Generation Partnership Project (3GPP). At that time, UMTS networks were rolled out worldwide and deployment of high speed downlink packet access (HSDPA) was about to begin. Although it might seem almost unbelievable from today's perspective, the mobile data take-up expected already from UMTS technology had not yet happened at that point in time.

On the other hand, technologies that were not part of the UMTS framework were appearing, the most prominent being WiMAX™. In order to ensure the competitiveness of UMTS over the coming years, the industry initiated work on UMTS long term evolution concepts. Their objective was to provide an impetus for UMTS towards a true mobile broadband technology supporting a high data rate, low latency and packet optimization. Given the long-term nature of the work, it was possible to deviate from existing technology paradigms and introduce new concepts.

The justification of the study item on E-UTRA and E-UTRAN reads as follows [Ref. 1].
With enhancements such as HSDPA and enhanced uplink, the 3GPP radio-access technology will be highly competitive for several years. However, to ensure competitiveness in an even longer time frame, i.e. for the next 10 years and beyond, a long-term evolution of the 3GPP radio-access technology needs to be considered.

Important parts of such a long-term evolution include reduced latency, higher user data rates, improved system capacity and coverage and reduced cost for the operator. In order to achieve this, an evolution of the radio interface as well as the radio network architecture should be considered.

Considering a desire for even higher data rates and also taking into account future additional 3G spectrum allocations the long-term 3GPP evolution should include an evolution towards support for wider transmission bandwidth than 5 MHz. At the same time, support for transmission bandwidths of 5 MHz and less than 5 MHz should be investigated in order to allow for more flexibility in whichever frequency bands the system may be deployed in.

The terms evolved UTRA(N) or E-UTRA(N) are widely used in 3GPP technical specifications, but the term long term evolution (LTE) has become synonymous for this technology as well.

2 Requirements and expectations for LTE

Obviously, LTE must satisfy ambitious demands in order to provide a technology that is ready for future requirements and lives up to industry expectations. Accordingly, the first part of 3GPP work involved the definition of clear requirements that LTE would have to fulfill. These requirements formed the baseline for the evaluation of new technology concepts, i.e. every new feature had to prove that it would contribute to the fulfillment of at least one of the requirements. Network operators in particular provided input on these requirements since it was in their vital interest to ensure an attractive long-term perspective for their existing UMTS networks with the associated return on investment.

The requirements identified by industry were captured in a technical report known as 3GPP TR 25.913 [Ref. 2]. Some major requirements are summarized as follows:

Packet switched services: LTE focuses solely on the packet switched domain and no longer supports circuit switched services. This implies support for voice services as voice over IP (VoIP).

Data rate: The requirement for the peak data rates was set to values of 100 Mbps in the downlink and 50 Mbps in the uplink, assuming a 20 MHz spectrum allocation and two receive antennas / one transmit antenna at the terminal. Note that these values were actually even exceeded by LTE specifications later. Peak data rates that can be achieved in LTE depending on the specified terminal categories are shown in 5.8, page 94. Although the achievable peak data rate is a typical parameter used to compare the performance of different wireless technologies, note that it cannot be used to derive individual data rates that users can expect to experience in the field. These values depend on a high number of different factors, including cell load, radio conditions, terminal capabilities, etc.

Throughput: The throughput requirement was derived based on performance of HSPA, i.e. the combination of HSDPA and HSUPA. The target for downlink average user throughput per MHz was expected to be 3–4 times better than HSPA in accordance with 3GPP release 6 specifications. The target for uplink average user throughput per MHz was expected to be 2–3 times better than HSPA release 6 specifications.

Spectrum efficiency: The target for downlink spectrum efficiency shall be 3–4 times better than HSPA in accordance with 3GPP release 6 specifications. The target for uplink spectrum efficiency shall be 2–3 times better than HSPA release 6.

Latency: Latency is an important measure for the interaction time between the subscriber and the network. In LTE, the one-way transit time between availability of a packet at the IP layer in either the terminal or radio access network and the availability of this packet at the IP layer in the radio access network or terminal shall be less than 5 ms. Moreover, control plane latency shall be low, e.g. to allow fast transition times of less than 100 ms to change the terminal from the camped state to the active state.

Bandwidth: There was a clear understanding from the beginning that LTE would operate in bandwidths up to 20 MHz and that scalable bandwidths should be supported with values smaller than this value. However, the final bandwidth parameterization was made much later in 3GPP. While the values of 5 MHz, 10 MHz, 15 MHz and 20 MHz were defined quite early, the smaller bandwidth values of 1.4 MHz and 3 MHz were not agreed upon for some time in the standardization groups. These smaller bandwidth values are important in order to allow operation of LTE in narrow spectral allocations.

Interworking: LTE must be able to interwork with existing UMTS and GSM/EDGE systems as well as with other "non-3GPP" systems. For example, WLAN, WiMAX™ and CDMA2000® 1xRTT/1x-EV-DO are referred to as "non-3GPP" systems since they are not specified in 3GPP working groups. During the course of work on LTE, interworking with CDMA2000® based networks became a very important requirement since major CDMA network operators worldwide decided to migrate to LTE. At the same time, interworking with WiMAX™ became less important. Interworking requirements have driven the need for corresponding multi-radio access technology (multi-RAT) terminals with support for inter-RAT measurements and handover functionality.

An associated requirement is the interruption time for the different handover types, which e.g. for the handover between E-UTRAN and UTRAN/GERAN shall be less than 300 ms for realtime services and less than 500 ms for non-realtime services.

Multimedia broadcast multicast services (MBMS): MBMS enables efficient support for point-to-multipoint transmission, e. g. for broadcast type services. In LTE, this is known as E-MBMS (enhanced MBMS). Due to the high workload in 3GPP, support for E-MBMS could not be completed within the 3GPP release 8 timeframe. Only some parts of the functionality remained in the release 8 specifications in order to enable introduction of full E-MBMS operation in 3GPP release 9.

Costs: Network operators expected LTE to become a cost-effective technology in terms of both capital and operational expenditures (CAPEX and OPEX) and also including backhaul considerations. This requirement especially reflects the lessons learned from the UMTS deployment. Moreover, migration from 3GPP release 6 UTRA radio interface and architecture to LTE shall be possible with reasonable effort and reasonable system and terminal complexity, cost and power consumption shall be ensured. Another important requirement addresses the multi-vendor capability of all of the interfaces specified since network operators desire a flexible choice of suppliers for different network entities.

Mobile speeds: LTE is optimized for low mobile speed (0–15 km/h), but higher mobile speeds shall also be supported including, for example, the high-speed train environment.

Duplex modes: Operation in paired (frequency division duplex, FDD) and unpaired spectrum (time division duplex, TDD) is possible. Accordingly, LTE includes an FDD mode of operation and a TDD mode of operation. The TDD mode is also referred to as TD-LTE. It provides the long term evolution path for TD-SCDMA based networks.

Quality of service: End-to-end quality of service (QoS) shall be supported. VoIP shall be supported with radio and backhaul efficiency and latency that is as least as good as voice traffic over UMTS circuit-switched networks.

Network synchronization: Time synchronization of different network sites shall not be mandated.

3   Technology selection process

The requirements contained in [Ref. 2] were taken as a basis for the LTE technology selection process, and especially for selecting the multiple access schemes on the air interface. This decision was by no means an easy one, and a careful evaluation phase preceded the final decision. In this phase, the following technology proposals were evaluated:

ı Orthogonal frequency division multiple access (OFDMA) in the downlink, single carrier frequency division multiple access (SC-FDMA) in the uplink
ı OFDMA in both downlink and uplink
ı Multicarrier-WCDMA (MC-WCDMA)

The first proposal was finally chosen. The technical reasons underlying this decision can be summarized as follows: OFDMA technology is highly efficient for mobile broadband operation and particularly robust under multipath fading conditions. Furthermore, it allows an efficient receiver architecture to be used in the terminal. OFDMA was therefore selected for the LTE downlink. The drawback of OFDM-type signals is that they can exhibit large crest factors which represent a challenge for power amplifier designers. For the uplink, this is crucial since the power amplifier design on the terminal side must not be overly complex or expensive. Therefore, SC-FDMA was selected for the LTE uplink. SC-FDMA can be considered as a precoded OFDMA technology. It yields lower crest factors. This is especially important for terminals at the cell edge. SC-FDMA thus also improves coverage. The drawback of SC-FDMA is the additional effort needed for precoding, which is effectively an additional discrete Fourier transform (DFT) operation on the terminal side.

This book focuses on the 3GPP release 8 specifications for LTE. A brief look at 3GPP release 9 and beyond, including LTE-Advanced, can be found in 7.1, page 178 and 7.2, page 184, respectively.

4 LTE network architecture / system architecture evolution

The term system architecture evolution (SAE) describes the evolution of the overall system architecture including the core network. SAE was defined by 3GPP along with the LTE radio network improvements. The new system architecture addresses the evolution of the 3GPP system to a system with a higher data rate, lower latency and packet optimization. The work on SAE was naturally heavily impacted by the decision to focus on the packet switched (PS) domain only. SAE also takes into account that legacy 2G/3G access networks have to be supported in terms of mobility and service continuity.

The evolved 3GPP packet-switched domain is also called the evolved packet system (EPS). Likewise, the evolved core network is also called the evolved packet core (EPC). The evolved radio access network is called evolved universal terrestrial radio access network (E-UTRAN). The radio access in general is described as evolved universal terrestrial radio access (E-UTRA). Fig. 4-1 shows the new LTE/SAE network architecture (simplified) and compares it with the legacy UMTS network architecture.

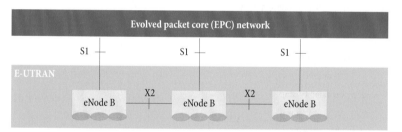

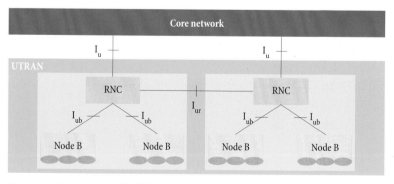

Fig. 4-1   Comparison of E-UTRAN and UTRAN.

Source: Rohde & Schwarz and [3GPP TS 25.401, Ref. 3], reproduced by permission of 3GPP

The LTE base stations form part of the E-UTRAN. They are called eNodeBs (eNBs) in the 3GPP standard. They provide the air interface user plane and control plane protocol terminations towards the terminal. This is a major change compared to previous UMTS standard releases where the radio access network consists of base station (NodeB) and radio network controller (RNC) entities and where the Iub interface connects the base stations with their RNC. This change has been made to provide a flat network architecture in LTE, allowing more cost-efficient network deployment and operation as well as improved network performance due to less overhead. The eNBs are directly connected to the EPC by means of the S1 interface.

The eNBs can be interconnected with each other by means of the X2 interface, e.g. to support communication and packet forwarding during handover. Note that the X2 interface is a logical interface so it does not have to be realized physically.

The EPC consists of different entities: The mobility management entity (MME), the serving gateway (S-GW) and the packet data network gateway (P-GW). Fig. 4-2 illustrates this structure as well as the functional split between E-UTRAN and the EPC entities.

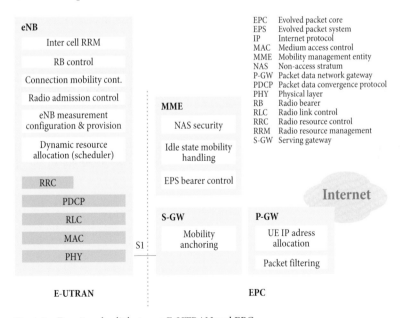

Fig. 4-2   Functional split between E-UTRAN and EPC.

Source: [3GPP TS 36.300, Ref. 4], reproduced by permission of 3GPP

The control protocols running between the terminal and the core network are called **non-access stratum (NAS)** protocols. On EPC side, they are terminated in the MME. The MME hosts functions for NAS signaling (e. g. detach / attach), NAS signaling security, tracking area list management, selection of P-GW and S-GW, inter-core-network node signaling for mobility between 3GPP access networks, authentication, bearer management functions, etc.

The S-GW is the gateway which terminates the S1 user plane interface towards E-UTRAN. It hosts packet processing functions such as packet routing and forwarding, charging, etc. Also, the S-GW is the mobility anchor point for inter-eNodeB handover, and provides mobility anchoring for inter-3GPP mobility (e. g. relaying traffic between the 2G / 3G network and P-GW). The S-GW and the MME may be implemented in one physical node or separate physical nodes.

The P-GW is the gateway which provides connectivity to external packet data networks. Its functions include per-user based packet filtering, UE IP address allocation, etc. S-GW and P-GW may be implemented in one physical node or separate physical nodes.

The following two figures show the overall protocol architecture for the **control plane** between UE and MME and the **user plane** between UE and P-GW. This book focuses on the radio protocols over the air interface (LTE-Uu). Their details will be explained in 5.6, page 61.

NAS	Relay		NAS
RRC	RRC	S1-AP	S1-AP
PDCP	PDCP	SCTP	SCTP
RLC	RLC	IP	IP
MAC	MAC	L2	L2
L1	L1	L1	L1
UE	**eNodeB**		**MME**
LTE-Uu		**S1-MME**	

Fig. 4-3   Control plane between UE and MME.

Source: [3GPP TS 23.401, Ref. 5], reproduced by permission of 3GPP

Abbreviations Fig. 4-3 and Fig. 4-4:

GTP	GPRS tunneling protocol	PDCP	Packet data convergence protocol
IP	Internet protocol	RLC	Radio link control
L1	Layer 1	RRC	Radio resource control
L2	Layer 2	S1-AP	S1 application protocol
MAC	Medium access control	SCTP	Stream control transmission protocol
NAS	Non-access stratum	UDP	User datagram protocol

Application						IP
IP						
PDCP	Relay		Relay		GTP-U	
	PDCP	GTP-U	GTP-U	GTP-U		
RLC	RLC	UDP/IP	UDP/IP	UDP/IP	UDP/IP	
MAC	MAC	L2	L2	L2	L2	
L1	L1	L1	L1	L1	L1	
UE	eNodeB		Serving GW		PDN GW	

LTE-Uu   S1-U   S5/S8   SGi

Fig. 4-4   User plane between UE and P-GW.

Source: [3GPP TS 23.401, Ref. 5], reproduced by permission of 3GPP

Due to the new LTE/SAE network architecture, the bearer architecture has also been modified. The term "bearer" as already used in UMTS/WCDMA represents a "connection" for information transfer between two endpoints and describes the level of granularity for quality of service (QoS) control. Each bearer provides a corresponding "bearer service", i.e. a transport service characterized by certain quality of service (QoS) attributes (scheduling weights, radio protocol configuration, etc.). The bearer architecture therefore describes the quality of service philosophy of LTE/SAE. It is illustrated in Fig. 4-5 with the components of an end-to-end service. For example, the base station is responsible for satisfying the QoS requirements of the radio bearer which transports packets of an E-UTRAN radio access bearer (E-RAB) between terminal and base station. The radio bearer is thus a component of the E-RAB, which itself is a component of the EPS bearer, which itself is a component of the end-to-end service.

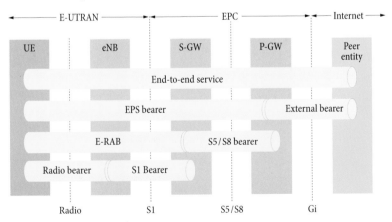

Fig. 4-5   Bearer architecture.

Source: [3GPP TS 36.300, Ref. 4], reproduced by permission of 3GPP

17

The EPS bearer is defined as the bearer between UE and P-GW. It uniquely identifies traffic flows that are subject to common QoS treatment and is therefore comparable to the packet data protocol (PDP) context that is familiar from the 2G/3G world. All traffic mapped to the same EPS bearer receives the same treatment in terms of scheduling policy, radio link control (RLC) configuration, etc.

One special EPS bearer known as the **default EPS bearer** is established when the terminal connects to a packet data network. It remains established throughout the life of the packet data network connection to provide the terminal with always-on IP connectivity. Any additional EPS bearer that is established to the same packet data network is referred to as a **dedicated bearer**. The decision to establish or modify a dedicated bearer can only be taken by the EPC, and the bearer level QoS parameter values are always assigned by the EPC.

Certain packet services may require a guaranteed bit rate (GBR) and the allocation of permanent network resources. Such an EPS bearer is referred to as a GBR bearer. For this bearer type, the base station is responsible on the E-UTRAN side for allocating radio resources to the radio bearer such that the guaranteed bit rate requirement is satisfied. EPS bearers not requiring a guaranteed bit rate are referred to as a non-GBR bearers. The default EPS bearer is always a non-GBR bearer.

5 Technical principles of the LTE air interface

5.1 Frequency bands

E-UTRA operating band	Uplink (UL) operating band BS receive; UE transmit F_{UL_low} to F_{UL_high}	Downlink (DL) operating band BS transmit; UE receive F_{DL_low} to F_{DL_high}	Duplex mode
1	1920 MHz to 1980 MHz	2110 MHz to 2170 MHz	FDD
2	1850 MHz to 1910 MHz	1930 MHz to 1990 MHz	FDD
3	1710 MHz to 1785 MHz	1805 MHz to 1880 MHz	FDD
4	1710 MHz to 1755 MHz	2110 MHz to 2155 MHz	FDD
5	824 MHz to 849 MHz	869 MHz to 894 MHz	FDD
6*	830 MHz to 840 MHz	875 MHz to 885 MHz	FDD
7	2500 MHz to 2570 MHz	2620 MHz to 2690 MHz	FDD
8	880 MHz to 915 MHz	925 MHz to 960 MHz	FDD
9	1749.9 MHz to 1784.9 MHz	1844.9 MHz to 1879.9 MHz	FDD
10	1710 MHz to 1770 MHz	2110 MHz to 2170 MHz	FDD
11	1427.9 MHz to 1447.9 MHz	1475.9 MHz to 1495.9 MHz	FDD
12	699 MHz to 716 MHz	728 MHz to 746 MHz	FDD
13	777 MHz to 787 MHz	746 MHz to 756 MHz	FDD
14	788 MHz to 798 MHz	758 MHz to 768 MHz	FDD
15	Reserved	Reserved	FDD
16	Reserved	Reserved	FDD
17	704 MHz to 716 MHz	734 MHz to 746 MHz	FDD
18	815 MHz to 830 MHz	860 MHz to 875 MHz	FDD
19	830 MHz to 845 MHz	875 MHz to 890 MHz	FDD
20	832 MHz to 862 MHz	791 MHz to 821 MHz	FDD
21	1447.9 MHz to 1462.9 MHz	1495.9 MHz to 1510.9 MHz	FDD
22	3410 MHz to 3490 MHz	3510 MHz to 3590 MHz	FDD
23	2000 MHz to 2020 MHz	2180 MHz to 2200 MHz	FDD
24	1626.5 MHz to 1660.5 MHz	1525 MHz to 1559 MHz	FDD
25	1850 MHz to 1915 MHz	1930 MHz to 1995 MHz	FDD
...			
33	1900 MHz to 1920 MHz	1900 MHz to 1920 MHz	TDD
34	2010 MHz to 2025 MHz	2010 MHz to 2025 MHz	TDD
35	1850 MHz to 1910 MHz	1850 MHz to 1910 MHz	TDD
36	1930 MHz to 1990 MHz	1930 MHz to 1990 MHz	TDD
37	1910 MHz to 1930 MHz	1910 MHz to 1930 MHz	TDD
38	2570 MHz to 2620 MHz	2570 MHz to 2620 MHz	TDD
39	1880 MHz to 1920 MHz	1880 MHz to 1920 MHz	TDD
40	2300 MHz to 2400 MHz	2300 MHz to 2400 MHz	TDD
41	2496 MHz to 2690 MHz	2496 MHz to 2690 MHz	TDD
42	3400 MHz to 3600 MHz	3400 MHz to 3600 MHz	TDD
43	3600 MHz to 3800 MHz	3600 MHz to 3800 MHz	TDD

Fig. 5-1 E-UTRA operating bands (* Band 6 is not applicable).

Source: [3GPP TS 36.101, release 10, Ref. 40], reproduced by permission of 3GPP

As an IMT-2000[1] technology and evolution of UMTS, LTE can be operated in the same bands as e.g. WCDMA / HSPA technology. In accordance with [3GPP TS 36.101, Ref. 6], LTE is designed to operate in the frequency bands listed in Fig. 5-1 which contains both FDD and TDD frequency bands. This table is still growing, i. e. further bands are added as spectrum is freed worldwide for next generation mobile communications technologies.

Of course, there are significant regional variations in terms of which bands are selected by network operators to deploy LTE. Moreover, operation of the higher LTE bandwidths up to 20 MHz is not possible everywhere. A terminal does not have to support all of these bands. Instead, a suitable combination is selected for each implementation depending on the respective market requirements so that roaming scenarios can also be supported efficiently.

5.2 Frame structure

As in UMTS WCDMA, LTE is based on 10 ms **radio frames.** Two frame structure types are defined for LTE: Frame structure type 1 for FDD mode and frame structure type 2 for TDD mode. For **frame structure type 1,** the 10 ms radio frame is divided into 20 equally sized slots of 0.5 ms. A subframe consists of two consecutive slots so that one radio frame contains ten subframes. This is illustrated in Fig. 5-2 (T_s = 32.55 ns reflects the basic time unit corresponding to 30.72 MHz).

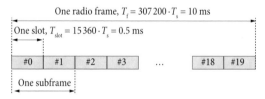

Fig. 5-2   Frame structure type 1 for FDD.

Source: [3GPP TS 36.211, Ref. 7], reproduced by permission of 3GPP

For **frame structure type 2,** the 10 ms radio frame consists of two half-frames of length 5 ms each. Each half-frame is divided into five sub-

---

1) International Mobile Telecommunications-2000 (IMT-2000) is the global standard for third generation (3G) wireless communications, defined by a set of interdependent ITU Recommendations.

frames of 1 ms each, as shown in Fig. 5-3. All subframes which are not "special subframes" are defined as two slots of length 0.5 ms. The special subframes consist of the three fields downlink pilot timeslot (DwPTS), guard period (GP) and uplink pilot timeslot (UpPTS). The names of these fields are familiar from TD-SCDMA and are maintained in LTE TDD. DwPTS and UpPTS are used for regular data and control transmissions, but some restrictions and special rules do apply to these fields. The guard period allows switching from downlink to uplink transmission.

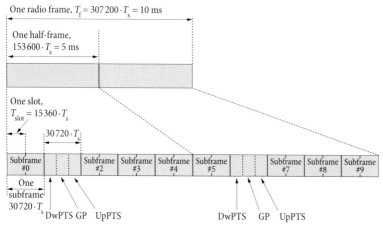

Fig. 5-3   Frame structure type 2 for TDD (for 5 ms switch-point periodicity).

Source: [3GPP TS 36.211, Ref. 7], reproduced by permission of 3GPP

DwPTS, GP and UpPTS have configurable individual lengths and a total length of 1 ms. Nine possible special subframe configurations 0 to 8 are defined and listed in Fig. 5-4 (for the case of normal cyclic prefix in downlink; the notion of cyclic prefix will be explained below in 5.3.1, page 23).

Special subframe config.	Normal cyclic prefix in downlink		
	DwPTS	UPTS	
		Normal cyclic prefix in uplink	Extended cyclic prefix in uplink
0	$6592 \cdot T_s$		
1	$19760 \cdot T_s$		
2	$21952 \cdot T_s$	$2192 \cdot T_s$	$2560 \cdot T_s$
3	$24144 \cdot T_s$		
4	$26336 \cdot T_s$		
5	$6592 \cdot T_s$		
6	$19760 \cdot T_s$	$4384 \cdot T_s$	$5120 \cdot T_s$
7	$21952 \cdot T_s$		
8	$24144 \cdot T_s$		

Fig. 5-4   Configuration of special subframe for normal cyclic prefix in downlink (T_s = 32.55 ns reflects the basic time unit).

Source: [3GPP TS 36.211, Ref. 7], reproduced by permission of 3GPP

The different special subframe configurations allow addressing of different cell sizes. For example, to accommodate a larger cell size a larger guard period is selected since uplink transmissions from terminals at the cell edge must also arrive at the base station in time and are adjusted accordingly.

TDD mode of operation with frame structure type 2 allows adaptation to different uplink-downlink traffic profiles by assigning more or less subframes within one radio frame for downlink or uplink data transmission. Seven uplink-downlink configurations with either 5 ms or 10 ms downlink-to-uplink switch-point periodicity are supported. In the case of 5 ms switch-point periodicity, the special subframe exists in both half-frames. In the case of 10 ms switch-point periodicity, the special subframe exists in the first half frame only. Subframes 0 and 5 and DwPTS are always reserved for downlink transmission. UpPTS and the subframe immediately following the special subframe are always reserved for uplink transmission. Fig. 5-5 shows the supported uplink-downlink configurations. Note that "D" denotes a subframe reserved for downlink transmission, "U" denotes a subframe reserved for uplink transmission and "S" denotes the special subframe.

Uplink-downlink configuration	Downlink-to-uplink switch-point periodicity	Subframe number									
		0	1	2	3	4	5	6	7	8	9
0	5 ms	D	S	U	U	U	D	S	U	U	U
1	5 ms	D	S	U	U	D	D	S	U	U	D
2	5 ms	D	S	U	D	D	D	S	U	D	D
3	10 ms	D	S	U	U	U	D	D	D	D	D
4	10 ms	D	S	U	U	D	D	D	D	D	D
5	10 ms	D	S	U	D	D	D	D	D	D	D
6	5 ms	D	S	U	U	U	D	S	U	U	D

Fig. 5-5   Uplink-downlink configurations for LTE TDD.

Source: [3GPP TS 36.211, Ref. 7], reproduced by permission of 3GPP

In practice, the selected uplink-downlink configuration may be a rather static configuration per cell in order to avoid interference effects which can occur e.g. if neighboring base stations have different uplink-downlink configurations. In this case, when one base station transmits and the other receives at a certain point in time, the receiving base station may be blocked by the other, especially in the case of a line-of-sight situation between the base stations.

5.3   Multiple access schemes

5.3.1   OFDMA in the downlink

LTE uses conventional OFDMA in the downlink. See e.g. [Ref. 8] for a general introduction to OFDM(A). The basic principle is illustrated in Fig. 5-6 with the example of a 5 MHz signal, but the scheme can be easily adapted to higher or lower bandwidths.

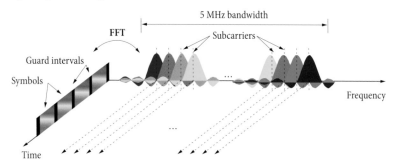

Fig. 5-6   Principle of OFDM(A) operation.

Source: [3GPP TR 25.892, Ref. 9], reproduced by permission of 3GPP

In an OFDM(A) system, the available transmission bandwidth is divided into subcarriers with equal spacing which can be independently modulated with data symbols. The high data rate stream is thus divided into several lower rate streams with longer symbol duration compared to a single-carrier transmission. This makes OFDM(A) transmission more robust in view of typical multipath propagation characteristics encountered in the mobile radio channel because the inter-symbol interference is reduced.

An important property of OFDM(A) transmission is the mathematical orthogonality of the subcarriers. This is achieved by selecting the subcarrier spacing in the manner shown in Fig. 5-6. At the center frequency of each subcarrier, the other subcarriers exhibit a zero-crossing in their sin(x)/x spectrum. This characteristic is inherent from the way the OFDM(A) signal is generated: The subcarriers are converted into a time-domain signal using an **inverse discrete Fourier transform** (IDFT) operation; see Fig. 5-7. The modulated data symbols are used as frequency bins for the IDFT and converted into time-domain OFDM symbols. The IDFT operation is typically realized as an inverse fast Fourier transform (IFFT). On the receiving end, an FFT operation is used to convert the time-domain symbols to the frequency domain so the subcarriers and the information they transport can be reseparated.

As shown in Fig. 5-6, the OFDM symbols transmitted in the time domain are separated by additional guard intervals to further protect the symbols from intersymbol interference. These guard intervals (or guard periods) decrease the sensitivity to the delay spread of the mobile radio channel. On the other hand, the guard interval must be considered as overhead since it cannot be used for transmission of information. As is common elsewhere, this guard interval is also realized in LTE using a **cyclic prefix (CP)** so that each OFDM symbol is preceded by a copy of the end part of the same symbol.

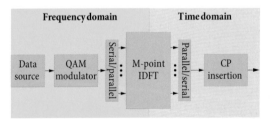

Fig. 5-7   OFDM signal generation based on IDFT operation.

The difference between OFDM and OFDMA lies in the scheduling. In OFDM, different users are scheduled in the time domain and always allocated the full available bandwidth. In OFDMA, users are scheduled in both the time and frequency domains so that several users can share the available bandwidth.

A particular benefit of OFDM(A) based systems is the frequency-dependent scheduling feature which allows adaptation of scheduling decisions in the frequency domain. For example, some subcarriers can be modulated with 64QAM while others are modulated with QPSK simultaneously in order to take frequency dependencies into account in the radio link quality. However, in LTE, the granularity for frequency-dependent scheduling does not exist on a subcarrier basis. This would involve too much signaling overhead at the expense of user data. For LTE, a trade-off between flexibility and complexity was selected.

Fig. 5-8 shows the structure of the LTE downlink resource grid for both FDD and TDD in the case of normal cyclic prefix. One subframe is shown. The x-axis shows the OFDM symbols in the time domain. The y-axis shows the subcarriers in the frequency domain. A resource element is formed by a combination of one specific OFDM symbol and one specific subcarrier.

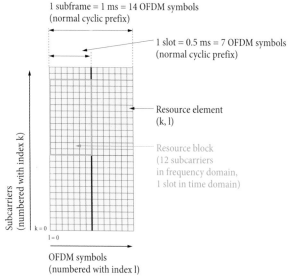

Fig. 5-8   Downlink resource grid.

The subcarriers in LTE have a constant spacing of Δf = 15 kHz. A particularly important definition in LTE is the resource block: It is defined by 12 contiguous subcarriers corresponding to 180 kHz in the frequency domain and one time slot in the time domain. The resource block is the smallest entity that can be scheduled in the frequency domain (in the downlink and uplink). This means that in the frequency domain, one terminal can receive or transmit in one resource block or integer multiples of one resource block only. In other words, it is not possible to assign less than 12 subcarriers to one terminal. The resource block size of 12 subcarriers corresponding to 180 kHz is the same for all bandwidths. The number of resource blocks for the different LTE bandwidths is listed in Fig. 5-9.

Channel bandwidth (MHz)	1.4	3	5	10	15	20
Number of resource blocks	6	15	25	50	75	100

Fig. 5-9   Number of resource blocks for different LTE bandwidths (FDD and TDD).

Source: [3GPP TS 36.101, Ref. 10], reproduced by permission of 3GPP

To each OFDM symbol, a cyclic prefix (CP) is appended as a guard interval (see Fig. 5-6) to protect the OFDM symbols against intersymbol interference. Different cyclic prefix lengths are available in LTE, i.e. a normal length and an extended length (a third extended length is also part of the release 8 specifications but not relevant for initial commercial operation; see 7.1.1, page 178). The extended cyclic prefix is able to cover larger cell sizes with higher delay spread of the radio channel. The delay spread of the radio channel is an important metric for characterizing the multipath propagation since it represents the difference between the first and last significant multipath components to arrive at the receiver.

With a larger cyclic prefix, less OFDM symbols can be accommodated within one slot. One downlink slot thus consists of 6 or 7 OFDM symbols depending on whether an extended or normal cyclic prefix is configured, respectively. The cyclic prefix lengths in samples and μs are summarized in Fig. 5-10.

Configuration	Resource block size in frequency domain	Number of symbols per slot	Cyclic prefix length	Cyclic prefix length
Normal cyclic prefix, Δf = 15 kHz	12 subcarriers	7	160 samples for first symbol, 144 samples for other symbols	5.2 μs for first symbol, 4.7 μs for other symbols
Extended cyclic prefix, Δf = 15 kHz	12 subcarriers	6	512 samples	16.7 μs

Fig. 5-10 Downlink frame structure parameterization (FDD and TDD).

Fig. 5-11 summarizes the scheduling principle of LTE. Data is allocated to terminals using **resource blocks** in the frequency domain. Note that these resource blocks are not necessarily adjacent to one other. In the time domain, the scheduling decision can be modified every transmission time interval of 1 ms. The scheduling decision is made in the base station (eNodeB). The scheduling algorithm must take into account the radio link quality situation of different users, the overall interference situation, quality of service requirements, service priorities, etc. Fig. 5-11 shows an example of allocation of downlink user data to different terminals (UE 1 to 6).

The user data is transported on the physical downlink shared channel (PDSCH); see 5.4.1, page 31 for more details on the downlink data and control channels.

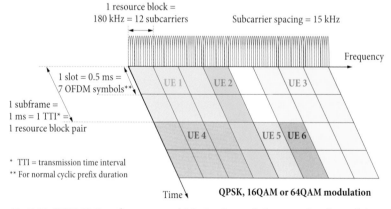

Fig. 5-11 OFDMA time-frequency multiplexing (example for normal cyclic prefix).

5.3.2 SC-FDMA in the uplink

In the LTE uplink, single carrier – frequency division multiple access (SC-FDMA) is used [Ref. 11]. The SC-FDMA scheme used in LTE can be best described as a precoded OFDM scheme. Compare the signal generation chains for SC-FDMA in Fig. 5-12 and for OFDM(A) in Fig. 5-7. SC-FDMA signal generation in the frequency domain is also based on an IDFT operation, but the modulated data symbols to be transmitted are not directly mapped to the IDFT. Instead, DFT pre-processing (or "precoding") is first performed on the modulated data symbols and its result is input to the IDFT stage. For this reason, SC-FDMA is also referred to as DFT-spread-OFDM (DFT-s-OFDM) or, as mentioned previously, precoded OFDM.

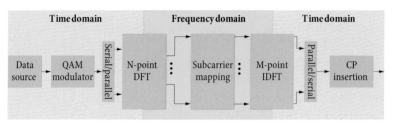

Fig. 5-12 SC-FDMA signal generation chain (in the LTE terminal).

What benefit is gained from the expense of an additional DFT stage in the terminal, compared to a classic OFDM scheme? The answer is that SC-FDMA significantly reduces the peak-to-average power ratio of the signal. Signals with a high peak-to-average power ratio degrade the efficiency of the terminal's power amplifiers. This is especially challenging for terminals at the cell edge. SC-FDMA is thus beneficial in terminal power amplifier design and contributes to improved uplink coverage. The achieved reduction of the peak-to-average power ratio depends on the signal parameterization in detail, e.g. on the modulation scheme, and can amount to more than 3 dB.

Due to similarities with the OFDM(A) signal generation chain, the parameterization of the LTE uplink is quite similar to the downlink. This is also true for the uplink frame structure. We are again referring to frame structure type 1 for FDD and frame structure type 2 for TDD. In frame structure type 1, an uplink radio frame consists of 20 slots of 0.5 ms each, and one subframe consists of two slots. The uplink structure is shown in Fig. 5-13.

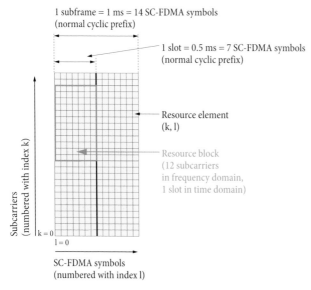

1 subframe = 1 ms = 14 SC-FDMA symbols
(normal cyclic prefix)

1 slot = 0.5 ms = 7 SC-FDMA symbols
(normal cyclic prefix)

Resource element
(k, l)

Resource block
(12 subcarriers
in frequency domain,
1 slot in time domain)

Subcarriers
(numbered with index k)

k = 0
l = 0

SC-FDMA symbols
(numbered with index l)

Fig. 5-13 Uplink resource grid.

For frame structure type 2, the selected uplink-downlink configuration determines the number of available uplink subframes; see Fig. 5-5. One radio frame contains one or two special subframes which include DwPTS, GP and UpPTS fields.

The notion of a **resource block** (12 subcarriers in the frequency domain, 1 slot in the time domain) is also defined in the uplink. It is the basic scheduling granularity in the frequency domain. In the time domain, the scheduling (or transmission time) interval is 1 ms corresponding to 1 subframe. Each 1 ms, the base station can convey a new scheduling decision to the terminal in the form of an uplink scheduling grant. The terminal then applies this grant a defined time interval later and adapts its uplink transmission on the physical uplink shared channel (PUSCH) accordingly. In FDD, this time interval corresponds to four subframes; in TDD, it is dependent on the configuration. The uplink scheduling mechanism is described in more detail in 5.7.3.2, page 79.

In contrast to the downlink, only consecutive (= localized) resource blocks can be assigned to the terminal in the uplink of release 8 LTE. Furthermore, not all integer multiples of one resource block can be assigned, but only those that are multiples of 2, 3 and 5. This lowers the complexity of the DFT design needed for SC-FDMA signal generation.

29

As in the downlink, different cyclic prefix configurations are defined to match different cell sizes. One slot carries 7 SC-FDMA symbols in the case of normal cyclic prefix configuration, and 6 SC-FDMA symbols in the case of extended cyclic prefix configuration. Fig. 5-14 shows the configuration parameters in an overview table.

Configuration	Number of symbols	Cyclic prefix length	Cyclic prefix length
Normal cyclic prefix, $\Delta f = 15$ kHz	7	160 samples for first symbol, 144 samples for other symbols	5.2 µs for first symbol, 4.7 µs for other symbols
Extended cyclic prefix, $\Delta f = 15$ kHz	6	512 samples	16.7 µs

Fig. 5-14 Uplink frame structure parameterization (FDD and TDD).

5.4 LTE physical channels and physical signals

One major objective in designing the LTE standard was to create a leaner protocol architecture with less transport and logical channels. This also impacts the physical layer: Less physical channel types are defined in LTE compared to WCDMA. The LTE physical channel design has to reflect the focus on packet-oriented data transmission. Transmission of data packets in LTE is based purely on shared channels in the uplink and downlink since they are optimized for the bursty traffic characteristics of IP data services. The radio link can be shared dynamically among the different cell users depending on their varying traffic needs and current radio conditions. Dedicated channels no longer exist in LTE.

Downlink shared channel transmission was already introduced with 3GPP release 5 in HSDPA. However, even in HSUPA of 3GPP release 6, uplink data transmission is still based on dedicated channels.

LTE downlink physical channels*	
Physical downlink shared channel (PDSCH)	Carries user data
Physical downlink control channel (PDCCH)	Carries control information (DCI = downlink control information)
Physical control format indicator channel (PCFICH)	Indicates the format of the PDCCH (CFI = control format indicator)
Physical hybrid ARQ indicator channel (PHICH)	Carries ACK/NACKs for uplink data packets (HI = HARQ indicator)
Physical broadcast channel (PBCH)	Provides information during cell search, e.g. on system bandwidth

LTE downlink physical signals	
Primary and secondary synchronization signals	Provide acquisition of cell timing and identity during cell search
Reference signal (RS)	Enables channel estimation

* Note: 3GPP release 8 also defines a physical multicast channel (PMCH) related to multimedia broadcast multicast services (MBMS). MBMS has been fully specified from 3GPP release 9 onwards and is therefore outside of the scope of this chapter. See 7.1.1, page 178 for more information.

Fig. 5-15 Overview of LTE downlink physical channels and physical signals.

LTE uplink physical channels	
Physical uplink shared channel (PUSCH)	Carries user data
Physical uplink control channel (PUCCH)	Carries control information (UCI = uplink control information)
Physical random access channel (PRACH)	Preamble transmission for initial access
LTE uplink physical signals	
Demodulation reference signal (DRS)	Enables channel estimation and data demodulation
Sounding reference signal (SRS)	Enables uplink channel quality evaluation

Fig. 5-16 Overview of LTE uplink physical channels and physical signals.

Fig. 5-15 and Fig. 5-16 summarize the LTE physical channels and physical signals. They are explained in more detail in the following chapters. A physical signal is defined solely inside the physical layer. In contrast to the physical signal, the content of a physical channel is provided by the higher layers.

5.4.1 LTE physical channels / signals in the downlink

The physical downlink shared channel (PDSCH) is used to carry downlink data packets, or more precisely, transport blocks that are passed down from layer 2 for transmission. Per transmission time interval of 1 ms and per terminal, one transport block can be transmitted in the case of SISO (up to two transport blocks are possible with MIMO spatial multiplexing mode, see 5.5, page 51). The PDSCH is shared dynamically among different users in a cell and can be compared to the high speed physical downlink shared channel (HS-PDSCH) from HSDPA.

Adaptive modulation and coding is used on the PDSCH so there is no fixed modulation and coding scheme defined for PDSCH. This means the base station can decide which modulation scheme and coding rate to use for a certain transmission depending on the radio link quality observed for a terminal. In terms of modulation schemes, QPSK, 16QAM and 64QAM can be used on PDSCH. PDSCH scheduling is based on resource blocks in the frequency domain, i.e. a PDSCH is always mapped to one or more resource blocks. The number of resource blocks needed for a transport block depends on the transport block size and the selected modulation scheme and coding rate.

The terminal naturally needs to be informed about the base station's decisions on scheduling and adaptive modulation and coding. Otherwise, the terminal would not know which resources are used to receive data packets along with the modulation and coding scheme for the transmission. For this purpose, a downlink control channel is associated with a PDSCH transmission. It must be read by the terminal before switching to the PDSCH resources. This is the **physical downlink control channel (PDCCH)**. Primarily, it is used to convey the scheduling decisions to individual terminals, i.e. scheduling assignments for the uplink and downlink, and to provide all of the information needed by the terminal to successfully receive and decode data packets. The terminal is addressed using a specific identifier (UE ID) so each terminal only has to decode messages on the PDCCH that are addressed to it.

This scheduling process is illustrated in Fig. 5-17 in a simplified manner:

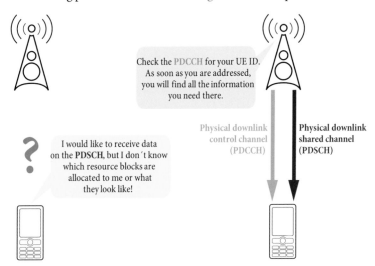

Fig. 5-17 Downlink scheduling process.

The PDCCH (or more specifically the PDCCHs since several terminals can be addressed within one subframe, each having its own PDCCH message) is located in the first OFDM symbols at the beginning of a subframe. For frame structure type 2, the PDCCH can also be mapped onto the first two OFDM symbols of the DwPTS field. In contrast to the PDSCH, the PDCCH is not mapped to full resource blocks in the frequency domain, but to specific resource elements inside the first OFDM symbols of the subframe in accordance with a pre-defined rule [Ref. 7]. PDCCH is QPSK modulated.

As was mentioned, several PDCCHs for different terminals can be sent per subframe. In order to make it easier for the terminal to find a PDCCH message addressed to it, the terminal does not have to scan all possible resource elements. Instead, a so-called "UE-specific search space" is defined which restricts the possible locations of a PDCCH for a certain terminal.

The control information that the PDCCH carries is called the down-link control information (DCI). Depending on the DCI format, i.e. the type of information conveyed on the PDCCH, the number of resource elements required for a PDCCH message varies. The number of PDCCHs also varies depending on the number of users in a cell. Therefore, the resource elements required to transmit all of the PDCCHs can vary greatly as well. In order to make it easier once again for the terminal to detect the PDCCH, an additional physical control format indicator channel (PCFICH) is defined. It is used to indicate the number of OFDM symbols required for the PDCCH (1, 2, 3 or 4 symbols are possible in a subframe). The PCFICH is carried on specific resource elements and only in the first OFDM symbol of the subframe. It is QPSK-modulated.

As was mentioned, depending on the purpose of the control message transmitted on the PDCCH, different DCI formats are defined in 3GPP TS 36.212 [Ref. 12]. By way of example, the content of DCI format 1 is shown in Fig. 5-18.

Information type	Number of bits on PDCCH	Purpose
Resource allocation header	1	Indicates whether resource allocation type 0 or 1 is used (see 5.7.3.1, page 72)
Resource block assignment	Depending on resource allocation type	Indicates resource blocks with PDSCH to be assigned to the terminal
Modulation and coding scheme	5	Indicates the modulation scheme and (in conjunction with the number of allocated physical resource blocks) the transport block size of the downlink packet
HARQ process number	3 (FDD), 4 (TDD)	Identifies the HARQ process the packet is associated with
New data indicator	1	Indicates whether the packet is a new transmission or a retransmission
Redundancy version	2	Identifies the redundancy version used for coding the transport block
TPC command for PUCCH	2	Transmit power control (TPC) command for adapting the transmit power on the physical uplink control channel (PUCCH)
Downlink assignment index (TDD only)	2	Number of downlink subframes for uplink ACK/NACK bundling

Fig. 5-18 Content of DCI format 1 carried on PDCCH.

DCI format 1 is used for the assignment of a downlink shared channel resource when no MIMO spatial multiplexing (see 5.5, page 51) is used. In this case, the scheduling information is provided for one transport block ("code word" in MIMO terminology) only. The information provided contains everything needed for the terminal to identify the resources for the PDSCH in that subframe along with how to decode it. Besides the downlink resource block assignment, this also includes information on the modulation and coding scheme and the hybrid ARQ protocol.

The cyclic redundancy check (CRC) for the DCI message is scrambled with the UE identity that is used to address the scheduled message to the terminal. This allows the terminal to unambiguously identify that the message is intended for itself.

As was mentioned, more DCI formats are defined for other use cases in order to optimize the PDCCH message size to the control information transmitted. Table 11 shows an overview of the possible DCI formats and their use cases.

DCI type	Content
DCI format 0	Uplink scheduling grant for PUSCH
DCI format 1	Scheduling of one PDSCH code word
DCI format 1A	Very compact scheduling of one PDSCH code word, or dedicated preamble assignment for initiating contention-free random access procedure; see 5.7.2, page 70
DCI format 1B	Compact scheduling of one PDSCH code word including MIMO precoding information, used for MIMO transmission mode 6; see 5.5.2, page 54
DCI format 1C	Very compact scheduling of one PDSCH code word, used for paging messages or system information (only QPSK modulation can be used)
DCI format 1D	Compact scheduling of one PDSCH code word including MIMO precoding and power offset information, needed for multi-user MIMO
DCI format 2	Scheduling of two PDSCH code words with closed loop spatial multiplexing
DCI format 2A	Scheduling of two PDSCH code words with open loop spatial multiplexing
DCI format 3	TPC commands for PUCCH and PUSCH with 2-bit power adjustment
DCI format 3A	TPC commands for PUCCH and PUSCH with single bit power adjustment

Fig. 5-19 Possible DCI formats carried on PDCCH.

Besides PCFICH and PDCCH, an additional downlink control channel is the physical hybrid ARQ indicator channel (PHICH). The PHICH is used to convey hybrid ARQ indicators (HIs), i.e. the acknowledgments / negative acknowledgments (ACK / NACKs) for the packets received in the uplink. See 5.7.4, page 83 on the uplink HARQ for more details. The PHICH is modulated with BPSK. It is mapped onto specific resource elements in the beginning of the subframe. For normal PHICH duration, the PHICH is found only within the first OFDM symbol of a subframe. For extended PHICH duration, the PHICH can be found in the first 3 OFDM symbols of a subframe (2 OFDM symbols in the case of subframes 1 and 6 for frame structure type 2). Higher layers configure the PHICH duration. Multiple PHICHs using different orthogonal sequences can be mapped onto the same resource elements (and can be distinguished by the respective orthogonal sequence). This is then known as a PHICH group.

Finally, the physical broadcast channel (PBCH) is defined as a physical channel. It carries the master information block which is part of the system information and transfers cell-specific information required by the terminal during the cell search (see 5.7.1, page 69). The PBCH is also modulated with QPSK and is always located in specific OFDM symbols in subframe 0. It is mapped onto the center 72 subcarriers, i.e. six resource blocks, in the frequency domain. The PBCH has a 40 ms transmission time interval, i.e. the terminal has to read 4 entities of the PBCH in 4 consecutive subframes before it can decode it. Fig. 5-20 illustrates the location of the PBCH in the time and frequency domains. A sequence of 10 subframes is shown based on the example of a 10 MHz LTE FDD signal with 50 resource blocks in the frequency domain. The PBCH can be seen in subframe 0 and the synchronization signals (described hereafter) in subframes 0 and 5.

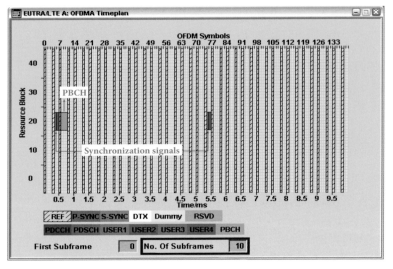

Fig. 5-20 Location of PBCH and synchronization signals in the time and frequency domains.

Let us now have a closer look at the physical signals in LTE. In the downlink, reference signals are carried on pre-defined resource elements. They are important for channel estimation on the terminal side. Fig. 5-21 illustrates the principle of the downlink reference signal structure in the case of a base station with 1-antenna, 2-antenna and 4-antenna transmission and for the case of a normal cyclic prefix. Specific pre-defined resource elements (indicated by R_{0-3}) in the time-frequency domain carry the cell-specific reference signal sequence. In the frequency domain, every sixth subcarrier carries a reference symbol. In the time domain, two OFDM symbols per slot carry reference symbols (except for antenna ports 2 and 3).

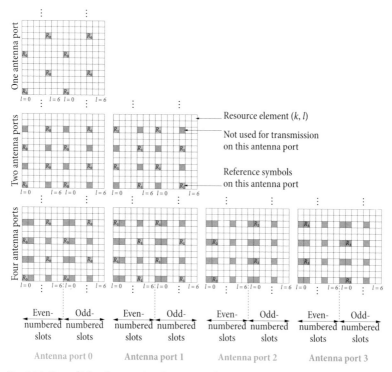

Fig. 5-21 **Downlink reference signal structure** for normal cyclic prefix.

Source: [3GPP TS 36.211, Ref. 7], reproduced by permission of 3GPP

The distribution of the reference signals is a trade-off. The closer the grid of resource elements carrying reference signals, the more accurate the channel estimation can be in frequency-selective channels, but the greater the overhead that is required.

The reference signal sequence is derived from a pseudorandom sequence [Ref. 7] and results in a QPSK type constellation. Cell-specific frequency shifts are applied when mapping the reference signal sequence to the subcarriers, i.e. the position in the frequency domain of the reference signals of different cells varies.

Synchronization signals are the second type of physical signals defined in LTE. They are needed during the first step in the cell search procedure. LTE uses a hierarchical cell search scheme similar to WCDMA. Thus, a **primary synchronization signal** and a **secondary synchronization signal** are defined. The synchronization signals are transmitted twice per 10 ms on predefined slots; see Fig. 5-22 for **FDD** and Fig. 5-23 for TDD. The PBCH structure in the time domain is also shown in these figures. In the frequency domain, the synchronization signals are transmitted on 62 subcarriers within 72 reserved subcarriers around the DC subcarrier.

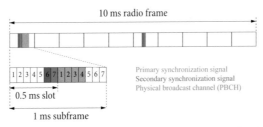

Fig. 5-22 Primary / secondary synchronization signal and PBCH structure (frame structure type 1 / FDD, normal cyclic prefix).

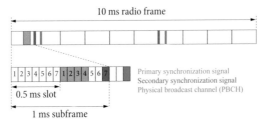

Fig. 5-23 Primary / secondary synchronization signal and PBCH structure (frame structure type 2 / TDD, normal cyclic prefix).

The 504 available LTE physical layer cell identities are grouped into 168 physical layer cell identity groups. Each group contains 3 unique identities (0, 1 or 2). The secondary synchronization signal carries the physical layer cell identity group and the primary synchronization signal carries the physical layer identity 0, 1 or 2.

The **primary synchronization signal** is based on a **Zadoff-Chu (ZC)** type of sequence [Ref. 13]. This is a special sequence type that is used for different purposes in LTE due to its favorable properties; see supplementary text in box below.

Zadoff-Chu sequences

Since Zadoff-Chu sequences form the basis for different physical signals in LTE (primary synchronization signal, PRACH, uplink reference signals, PUCCH), their generation and properties are discussed here. A so-called Zadoff-Chu sequence $x_u(m)$ of root u and length N_{ZC} is generated with the following formula:

$$x_u(m) = e^{-j\frac{\pi u m(m+1)}{N_{ZC}}}, 0 \leq m \leq N_{ZC} - 1$$

This results in a sequence of N_{ZC} complex values. Based on this "root sequence", further sequences can be defined by cyclically shifting the root sequence. These cyclic-shifted versions are then orthogonal to each other.

Zadoff-Chu sequences are constant amplitude zero auto-correlation (CAZAC) sequences. The "zero auto-correlation" property means that the periodic autocorrelation function is zero except for the zero shift value. This is a characteristic which is beneficial for detecting the sequence at a receiver and for time localization.

For the primary synchronization signal, three different sequences (with different root index) exist corresponding to the physical layer identities 0, 1 or 2. The resulting constellation for the three different sequences is shown in Fig. 5-24.

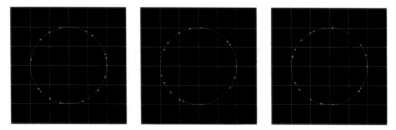

Fig. 5-24 Constellation diagram of the three different primary synchronization signal sequences. Note: The brighter green points are actually a conglomerate of several single constellation points.

The secondary synchronization signal is based on an interleaved concatenation of two length-31 binary sequences, resulting in a BPSK type of modulation; see Fig. 5-25. The selection of this sequence type was made to optimize detection of the secondary synchronization signal during cell search. Since the mapping of the secondary synchronization signal is different in subframe 0 and 5, the terminal can identify the radio frame timing by detecting the secondary synchronization signal. For the terminal to support this concept of physical signals and channels for cell search, each LTE terminal must support a minimum bandwidth reception capability of 20 MHz.

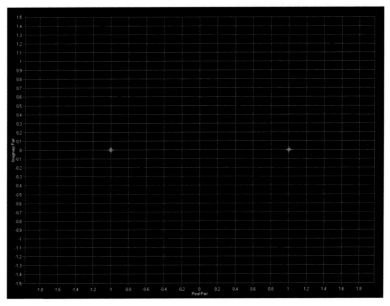

Fig. 5-25 Constellation diagram of the secondary synchronization signal.

5.4.2 LTE physical channels / signals in the uplink

Unlike HSPA, the LTE uplink is also based on shared channel transmission. Again, this optimizes the transmission characteristics for packet-oriented traffic. The physical uplink shared channel (PUSCH) is used to carry uplink data packets, i.e. transport blocks that are passed from layer 2 to layer 1 (physical layer) for transmission. One transport block per transmission time interval of 1 ms per terminal can be transmitted in the uplink. The PUSCH is dynamically shared among different users in a cell. The uplink scheduling grant contained in DCI format 0 on the PDCCH informs the terminals when they are allowed to transmit in the uplink and which modulation and coding scheme to use for transmission. For the modulation scheme, QPSK, 16QAM and 64QAM can be used on the PUSCH. However, 64QAM is optional for the terminal to support; it is a UE capability and only supported by UE category 5 (see 5.8, page 94). PUSCH scheduling is based on resource blocks in the frequency domain, i. e. a PUSCH is always mapped onto one or more consecutive resource blocks.

The physical uplink control channel (PUCCH) enables the transport of different types of uplink control information (UCI) from the terminal to the base station:

ı Acknowledgments / negative acknowledgments (ACK / NACK) related to data packets received in the downlink; this can also be ACK / NACK information for two data packets (i. e. code words) in the case of MIMO spatial multiplexing
ı Channel quality indicator (CQI) reports to provide feedback to the base station about the downlink radio link quality experienced by the terminal
ı Precoding matrix information (PMI) and rank indication (RI) to support MIMO mode selection and configuration; see 5.5, page 51
ı Scheduling requests (SR) for requesting additional uplink resources

Note that a terminal uses the PUCCH only when it does not have any data to transmit on the PUSCH at that time. If a terminal has data to transmit on the PUSCH, it multiplexes the above-mentioned uplink control information with the data on the PUSCH.

The PUCCH is transmitted in a reserved frequency region, i. e. reserved resource blocks, at both edges of the uplink channel bandwidth. Higher layers configure how many resource blocks are reserved for the PUCCH. Inter-slot hopping is used on the PUCCH, i. e. the PUCCH hops from a resource block at one edge of the bandwidth to a resource block at the other edge of the bandwidth within one subframe. This provides frequency diversity. Fig. 5-26 illustrates PUCCH resource allocation, e. g. a 10 MHz FDD signal with 50 resource blocks. One resource block is allocated for PUCCH at the edge of the bandwidth, and inter-slot hopping is applied. Note that several users can be multiplexed on this PUCCH resource. For TDD, the PUCCH can be transmitted only in regular uplink subframes and not on UpPTS.

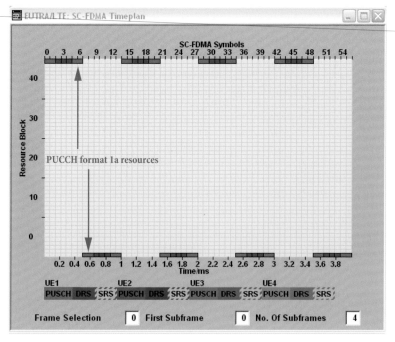

Fig. 5-26 Example of PUCCH resource allocation (format 1a).

In accordance with the different types of information that the PUCCH can carry, different PUCCH formats are specified; see Fig. 5-27. They differ in terms of the modulation scheme, number of bits per subframe and reference symbol positions. PUCCH formats 1, 1a and 1b have three reference symbols (the third through the fifth symbol) per slot for the normal cyclic prefix (see Fig. 5-26), while PUCCH formats 2, 2a and 2b have only two reference symbols (the second and the sixth symbol) per slot for the normal cyclic prefix.

The uplink control information (e.g. one entity of ACK / NACK information) is processed in the transmitter and then mapped onto the available symbols and subcarriers within a PUCCH resource block pair. The PUCCH transmissions of different terminals can be multiplexed onto the same PUCCH resource block pair since each terminal multiplies its transmission with a specific cyclic shift of a (Zadoff-Chu type) sequence; see 5.4.1, page 31. The cyclic shift varies per symbol and slot. Higher layers may restrict employment of all 12 possible cyclic shifts of the sequence used for PUCCH depending on radio channel conditions. Channels with large delay spread can degrade the orthogonality between the cyclically shifted sequences since the signals arriving at the base station receiver must not have an excessively large time difference.

PUCCH format	Content	Modulation scheme	Number of bits per subframe
1	Scheduling request (SR)	N/A	N/A (information is indicated by the presence or absence of transmission: in the case of positive SR transmission, one modulation symbol is transmitted on the PUCCH)
1a	ACK / NACK, ACK / NACK + SR	BPSK	1
1b	ACK / NACK, ACK / NACK + SR	QPSK	2
2	CQI / PMI or RI (any cyclic prefix), (CQI / PMI or RI) + ACK / NACK (extended cyclic prefix only)	QPSK	20
2a	(CQI / PMI or RI) + ACK / NACK (normal cyclic prefix only)	QPSK + BPSK	21
2b	(CQI / PMI or RI) + ACK / NACK (normal cyclic prefix only)	QPSK + QPSK	22

Fig. 5-27 PUCCH formats and content.

For PUCCH formats 1/1a/1b with only one modulation symbol to be transmitted, orthogonality between users is further improved by a spreading operation with orthogonal codes of spreading factor 4.

Some resource blocks that are available for PUCCH can be reserved by the higher layers for PUCCH format 2/2a/2b transmission only. One resource block can also be configured to allow a mix of PUCCH format 1/1a/1b and PUCCH format 2/2a/2b. The allocation of several PUCCH resource block pairs within one subframe is illustrated in Fig. 5-28. The available resource block pair (index m) that is actually used for a certain PUCCH transmission is derived from the PUCCH format and the exact PUCCH resource index that the terminal uses [Ref. 7].

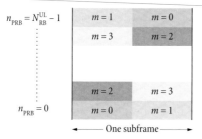

Fig. 5-28 PUCCH resource block pairs
(PRB = physical resource block, N_{RB}^{UL} = number of resource blocks for uplink bandwidth configuration).
Source: [3GPP TS 36.211, Ref. 7], reproduced by permission of 3GPP

Depending on the type of uplink control information to be transmitted, the terminal must use the correct PUCCH format and determine the resource index within this format. The PUCCH content determines how the terminal derives the exact PUCCH resource index. For ACK / NACK in response to a PDSCH transmission, the terminal derives the PUCCH resource index to use from the PDCCH transmission (or more precisely, from the number of the first control channel element (see 5.7.3.1, page 72) used for transmission of the corresponding downlink resource assignment, plus from a layer 3 parameter (*n1PUCCH-AN*) configured by the higher layers). When the terminal has a scheduling request or CQI / PMI or RI to send, the higher layers will configure the exact PUCCH resource to use.

For PUCCH format 1, information is carried by the presence / absence of PUCCH transmission from the terminal for the assigned PUCCH resource index. For PUCCH formats 1a and 1b when both ACK / NACK and SR are transmitted in the same subframe, the UE shall transmit ACK / NACK on its assigned ACK / NACK resource in the case of negative SR transmission and transmit ACK / NACK on its assigned SR resource in the case of positive SR transmission.

Uplink reference signal structure

There are two types of uplink reference signals specified in LTE:

The demodulation reference signal (DRS) is used for channel estimation in the base station receiver in order to demodulate control and data channels. For PUSCH, it is located on the 4th symbol in each slot (for normal cyclic prefix) and spans the same bandwidth as the allocated uplink data. For PUCCH, the reference signal location depends on the PUCCH format used (see above).

The sounding reference signal (SRS) enables the base station to derive uplink channel quality information as a basis for scheduling decisions. The terminal sends a sounding reference signal in different parts of the bandwidths and also in frequency regions where no uplink data transmission is available on the PUSCH from this particular terminal. If configured, the sounding reference signal is transmitted in the last symbol of the subframe. For TDD, the sounding reference signal can occur in regular subframes as well as in UpPTS. The configuration of the sounding signal, e.g. the bandwidth, duration and periodicity, is determined by the higher layers.

Both uplink reference signals are derived from so-called Zadoff-Chu (ZC) sequence types which are also used for the downlink primary synchronization signal (see 5.4.1, page 31) and for PUCCH and PRACH preambles; (described in this chapter). Reference signals for different terminals are derived using different cyclic shifts from the same base sequence. Fig. 5-29 shows the constellations of two sample uplink reference signals which were generated using two different cyclic shifts of the same sequence.

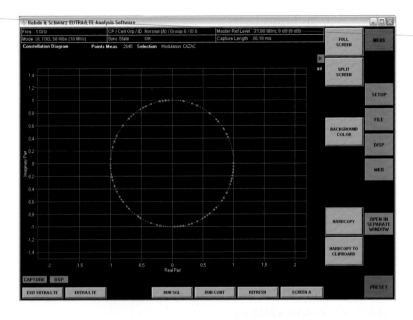

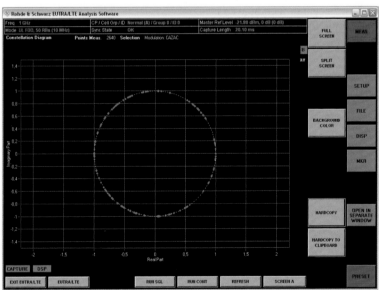

Fig. 5-29 Uplink reference signal sequences for an allocation of eleven resource blocks, generated using different cyclic shifts of the same base sequence.

As there are several sequences available for each required sequence length (corresponding to different resource block allocations), the available base sequences are divided into 30 groups identified by a sequence group number u. The group number to be used by a cell is configured by the higher layers and determines the available reference signal sequences on the cell level. Within a group, there is a reference signal sequence for each resource block allocation size ($v = 0$). Moreover for allocations of more than five resource blocks, there is an additional second sequence ($v = 1$). The sequence group number u and the number within the group v may vary in time. This is known as group hopping and sequence hopping, respectively. These schemes help to mitigate intercell interference effects.

Group hopping is switched on or off by the higher layers (parameter *groupHoppingEnabled*). If it is used, the sequence group number u needed in a certain timeslot is controlled by a pre-defined pattern configured by the higher layers.

Sequence hopping applies only for uplink resource allocations of more than five resource blocks. If it is enabled (by the higher layers using the parameter *sequenceHoppingEnabled*), the base sequence number v within the group u changes on a slot basis.

Multiple reference signal sequences for different terminals can be derived from one base sequence by using different cyclic shifts. The exact cyclic shift to use for the uplink reference signal sequence is calculated by the terminal via the parameter *cyclic shift for DM RS* as part of the scheduling grant in DCI format 0 and via the layer 3 parameter *cyclicShift* (0 to 7).

The sounding reference signal is also based on cyclic shifts of a Zadoff-Chu type of sequence. The cyclic shift to be used by a terminal is configured by the higher layers. Sequence group number u and base sequence number v are the same as that derived for the PUCCH reference signal in a slot. The sounding reference signal is highly configurable in terms of how often it is sent, the bandwidth it spans, etc. Different basic sounding bandwidth configurations can be selected by the network for a cell and further adapted for a specific terminal. Frequency hopping can be configured additionally by the higher layers. Note that the sounding reference signal is not transmitted on every subcarrier of the allocated resource blocks, but only on every second subcarrier. The layer 3 parameter *transmissionComb* (0 or 1) tells the terminal which set of subcarriers to use.

In terms of the timing, the network can configure a certain basic sub-frame configuration for the sounding reference signal per cell, and additional terminal-specific constraints can be provided as well. The SRS transmissions can be configured to occur periodically between 2 ms and 320 ms.

For examples of possible sounding reference signal configurations see Fig. 5-30 through Fig. 5-32. Fig. 5-30 shows a configuration without frequency hopping and Fig. 5-31 a configuration with frequency hopping. Both configurations have a periodicity for the sounding reference signal of 2 ms. Fig. 5-32 shows another example of a frequency hopping sounding reference signal but with a higher sounding bandwidth and a periodicity of 5 ms. All of the examples are based on an FDD 10 MHz signal.

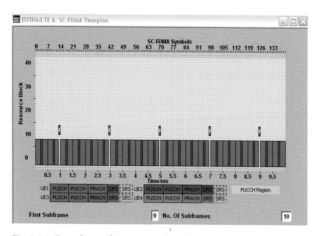

Fig. 5-30 Sounding reference signal configuration, no frequency hopping.

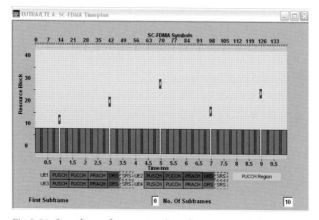

Fig. 5-31 Sounding reference signal configuration, with frequency hopping.

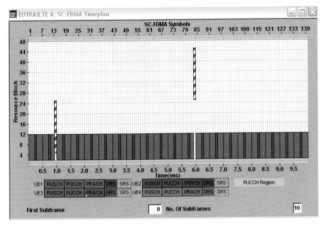

Fig. 5-32 Sounding reference signal configuration, with frequency hopping.

The physical random access channel (PRACH) is used for initial access to a cell. The PRACH is sent as a preamble with the structure shown in Fig. 5-33. The preamble consists of a sequence with length T_{SEQ} and a cyclic prefix with length T_{CP}.

Fig. 5-33 Random access preamble.

Source: [3GPP TS 36.211, Ref. 7], reproduced by permission of 3GPP

For frame structure type 1, four different preamble formats are defined with different T_{SEQ} and T_{CP} values. The different lengths reflect configurations for different cell sizes and environments. An additional shorter preamble format 4 is defined for frame structure type 2 for usage in the UpPTS field in the special subframe. See Fig. 5-34 for the different random access preamble formats. Preamble formats 2 and 3 actually repeat the preamble for improved protection in high path loss scenarios. Preamble formats 1 and 3 have a longer cyclic prefix which is beneficial in scenarios exhibiting larger delay spread in the radio channel.

Preamble format	T_{CP}	T_{SEQ}	Total length	Subcarrier spacing
0	$3168 \cdot T_s$	$24576 \cdot T_s$	0.903 ms	1.25 kHz
1	$21024 \cdot T_s$	$24576 \cdot T_s$	1.484 ms	1.25 kHz
2	$6240 \cdot T_s$	$2 \cdot 24576 \cdot T_s$	1.803 ms	1.25 kHz
3	$21024 \cdot T_s$	$2 \cdot 24576 \cdot T_s$	2.284 ms	1.25 kHz
4	$448 \cdot T_s$	$4096 \cdot T_s$	0.148 ms	7.5 kHz

Fig. 5-34 Random access preamble formats.

Source: [3GPP TS 36.211, Ref. 7], reproduced by permission of 3GPP

In the frequency domain, the random access preamble is transmitted within a bandwidth of six resource blocks, i.e. 1.08 MHz.

The PRACH can be sent only on pre-defined time and frequency resources so as to avoid collision with regular uplink transmissions. The parameters *prach-ConfigIndex* and *prach-FreqOffset* provided by the higher layers define the PRACH configuration in terms of time and frequency. While for FDD there can be at most one PRACH resource per subframe, there can be multiple random access resources per subframe for TDD depending on the UL/DL configuration.

Per cell, there are 64 random access **preambles**. They are generated from Zadoff-Chu (ZC) type sequences. The 64 preambles per cell are generated using cyclic shifts of a root ZC sequence which is indicated by the higher layers per cell (and an additional second root ZC sequence in case the first sequence does not allow derivation of the required 64 preambles). In the case of high-speed scenarios, the set of preambles to be used can be further restricted in order to prevent deterioration of the correlation properties due to the Doppler effect. This can be configured by the network by setting the layer 3 parameter *highSpeedFlag* to true.

The available PRACH preambles may be further divided into two groups A and B which can be configured by the base station. If the terminal expects to transmit a larger message size within the random access procedure (message 3; see 5.7.2, page 70), then it will select a preamble from group B. The base station can then prepare to allocate sufficient uplink resources for this terminal. The threshold of the message size to select group B preambles is also configured by the higher layers. Within the selected group, the terminal randomly selects the available preamble for initial access.

Note that the network can reserve a certain number of preambles for contention-free access and also certain PRACH resources, e.g. to be used during handover.

5.5 MIMO antenna technology

5.5.1 Introduction and general definitions

Multiple input multiple output (MIMO) antenna technology is a key feature for the LTE downlink: MIMO provides the only way to fulfill the ambitious targets for the data rate and throughput. There is not just a single MIMO configuration in LTE. Instead, different downlink MIMO modes are specified for LTE which can be adjusted and flexibly configured in accordance with channel conditions, data rate requirements and UE capabilities. Note that this full selection of MIMO options is available only for the downlink in LTE. In order to limit terminal complexity, these options are not yet available in the uplink of LTE release 8.

For understanding LTE MIMO concepts, it is useful to understand the following terms:

Spatial multiplexing: This technique is sometimes referred to as "true MIMO". It enables an increase in a terminal's data rate over the air interface. Different streams of data are simultaneously transmitted over the same set of radio resources; see Fig. 5-35. In other words, spatial re-use of the radio resources becomes possible. The maximum number of streams that can be multiplexed depends on the antenna configuration: In a 2×2 scenario with two transmit and two receive antennas, up to two streams can be spatially multiplexed; in a 4×4 scenario with four transmit and four receive antennas, up to four streams can be spatially multiplexed. Note that the use of spatial multiplexing is restricted by the channel conditions. If the transmissions over the different antennas are too correlated, spatial multiplexing does not work. This is assessed by evaluating the MIMO channel matrix. It contains the channel impulse responses h_{ij} for each channel that is formed by a combination of one transmit antenna j and one receive antenna i; see Fig. 5-35.

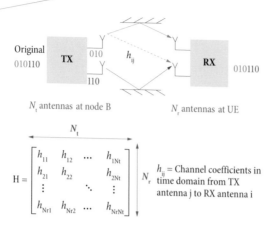

Fig. 5-35 Principle of spatial multiplexing and MIMO channel matrix H. Note: For the sake of simplicity, the time variance of the channel matrix is neglected in this illustration.

If the data streams that are spatially multiplexed belong to one user, this is referred to as **single-user MIMO (SU-MIMO)**. If the data streams that are spatially multiplexed belong to different users, this is referred to as **multi-user MIMO (MU-MIMO)**. While single-user MIMO directly impacts the data rate of the user, multi-user MIMO is a technique that helps to increase the capacity of the cell.

Rank (of the channel matrix): The channel matrix H is estimated in the terminal receiver by estimating the channels created by the combinations of one transmit and one receive antenna. The rank of a matrix defines the number of linearly independent columns and rows and therefore helps to determine whether a system of linear equations can be solved (in the case of MIMO to detect the spatially multiplexed data streams on the receiver side). Therefore, the rank of the channel matrix determines whether spatial multiplexing is possible under the given channel conditions and, if so, how many data streams can be spatially multiplexed. If the matrix does not have full rank, the channels are too spatially correlated so that spatial multiplexing either will not work at all, or only with a reduced number of spatially multiplexed data streams. This information is made available to the base station via the uplink control signaling so the base station can then suitably adapt the MIMO mode and configuration for the upcoming downlink transmissions. This is also referred to as "rank adaptation".

Transmit diversity: This technique is another major "MIMO mode" used in LTE. It was already introduced in UMTS WCDMA from release 99 onwards, but LTE uses a different flavor of it. In the case of transmit diversity, the base station antennas transmit the same data streams simultaneously, i.e. replicas of the same signal. Each antenna uses a different coding, but the information content that is transmitted remains the same. Thus, transmit diversity does not increase the data rate, but it does increase the robustness of the transmission, e.g. against fading, by exploiting the diversity effect. A common scheme used for transmit diversity is the so-called **Alamouti** coding [Ref. 14] which is also the basis for the **space-frequency block coding (SFBC)** scheme used in LTE.

(Spatial) layer: The definition of the term "layer" is different for spatial multiplexing and transmit diversity:

ı In the case of spatial multiplexing, the term "layer" indicates how many spatial streams can be simultaneously transmitted over the air interface. The number of layers v is less than or equal to the number of transmit antenna ports and depends on the rank of the channel matrix.

ı In the case of transmit diversity, only one data stream can be transmitted and the number of layers v is equal to the number of transmit antenna ports.

Code word: A code word is a block of information bits that can be encoded, scrambled and modulated separately before it is transmitted in a subframe over the air interface. One code word corresponds to one transport block provided by the MAC layer. In LTE, up to two code words can be spatially multiplexed, i.e. they can be transmitted simultaneously over the same radio resource. This provides more coding flexibility compared to the case in which only one code word can be transmitted which is split up over different spatial layers.

In the case of spatial multiplexing with two transmit antennas, two code words are mapped onto two spatial layers, or one code word is mapped onto one spatial layer. In the case of spatial multiplexing with four transmit antennas, more cases are possible: One code word can be mapped onto one layer or onto two layers. Two code words can be mapped onto two, three or four layers. In the case of transmit diversity, only one code word can be transmitted.

Cyclic delay diversity (CDD): Cyclic delay diversity is an additional type of diversity which in LTE can be used in conjunction with open loop spatial multiplexing. An antenna-specific delay is applied to the signals transmitted from each antenna port. To be more precise, cyclically delayed copies of the same signal are transmitted over the different antenna ports. This cyclic delay effectively introduces artificial multipath to the signal as seen by the receiver. By doing so, the frequency diversity of the radio channel is artificially increased. The optimum delay value depends on the radio channel conditions and the mobile speed. In LTE, a so-called "large delay" cyclic delay diversity scheme is defined indicating the dimensioning of the delay parameter for high mobile speed scenarios and maximizing the frequency diversity effect.

5.5.2 Downlink MIMO in LTE

LTE uses a wide selection of MIMO modes and configuration options for the PDSCH. The physical channels PBCH, PHICH, PCFICH and PDCCH are restricted to usage of transmit diversity. In the following, focus is on the PDSCH. This book only provides an overview of the MIMO aspects of LTE with some of the aspects highlighted.

LTE defines the following MIMO modes for use on the PDSCH in 3GPP release 8 [TS 36.213, Ref. 15]:
I Mode 1: Single-antenna transmission, no MIMO
I Mode 2: Transmit diversity
I Mode 3: Selection of transmit diversity or open-loop spatial multiplexing with large delay CDD
I Mode 4: Selection of transmit diversity or closed-loop spatial multiplexing
I Mode 5: Selection of transmit diversity or multi-user MIMO
I Mode 6: Selection of transmit diversity or closed-loop spatial multiplexing using a single transmission layer
I Mode 7: Beamforming. Note: This transmission mode is called "single-antenna port; port 5" in [Ref. 15] since from the terminal's perspective the beamformed PDSCH appears to originate from one transmit antenna port.

The higher layers configure which of the above-mentioned MIMO modes is used in terminal-specific signaling. The MIMO mode also influences the downlink control information (DCI) format (see 5.4.1, page 31) that is used since each MIMO mode requires a different type and amount of control signaling to be conveyed to the terminal. For example, in the case of spatial multiplexing, the DCI needs to indicate the control information for two code words, while for transmit diversity, the control information refers only to one code word.

Fig. 5-36 gives an overview of LTE downlink signal generation in the base station, including the steps relevant for MIMO transmission, i.e. the layer mapper and the precoding stage. The layer mapper and the precoding stage are influenced by the selection of the MIMO mode.

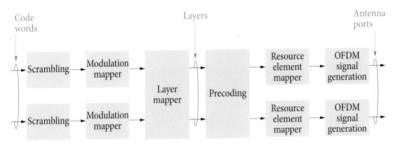

Fig. 5-36 LTE downlink transmission chain.

Source: [3GPP TS 36.211, Ref. 7], reproduced by permission of 3GPP

One or two **code words** are transmitted and can be scrambled and modulated separately. The modulation mapper provides modulation symbols in accordance with the possible downlink modulation schemes QPSK, 16QAM or 64QAM. The modulation symbols for the code word(s) are then mapped onto layers. How the code words are mapped onto layers is precisely specified [Ref. 7]:

ı For spatial multiplexing, a single code word can be mapped onto one or two layers (the latter case is applicable only to four transmit antennas). Two code words can be mapped onto two, three or four layers (the latter two cases are applicable only to four transmit antennas).

ı For transmit diversity, one code word is mapped either onto two or four layers (i.e. transmit antennas).

Precoding
The layer symbols are not mapped directly onto the antenna ports. Instead, a precoding stage as shown in Fig. 5-36 is used to define the mapping onto the antenna ports and make it possible to apply an addi-

tional antenna-specific coding. Precoding is achieved by multiplying the signal with a precoding matrix W before transmission. This can also be described as a type of beamforming where antenna-specific weighting is applied to the signal before transmission. However, beam-forming is mostly associated with forming more or less precise beams in the antenna radiation pattern, which is not necessarily observed with precoding in general.

For spatial multiplexing, the optimum precoding matrix W is selected from a predefined "codebook" which is known on the base station and terminal ends. The codebook for the case of two transmit antennas in LTE is shown in Fig. 5-37. The preferred pre-coding matrix within the given codebook is the one which offers maximum reception quality to the terminal.

Codebook index	Number of layers v	
	1	2
0	$\frac{1}{\sqrt{2}}\begin{bmatrix} 1 \\ 1 \end{bmatrix}$	$\frac{1}{\sqrt{2}}\begin{bmatrix} 1 & 0 \\ 0 & 1 \end{bmatrix}$
1	$\frac{1}{\sqrt{2}}\begin{bmatrix} 1 \\ -1 \end{bmatrix}$	$\frac{1}{2}\begin{bmatrix} 1 & 1 \\ 1 & -1 \end{bmatrix}$
2	$\frac{1}{\sqrt{2}}\begin{bmatrix} 1 \\ j \end{bmatrix}$	$\frac{1}{2}\begin{bmatrix} 1 & 1 \\ j & -j \end{bmatrix}$
3	$\frac{1}{\sqrt{2}}\begin{bmatrix} 1 \\ -j \end{bmatrix}$	–

Fig. 5-37 Precoding codebook for the case of two transmit antennas and spatial multiplexing.

Source: [3GPP TS 36.211, Ref. 7], reproduced by permission of 3GPP

The codebook in Fig. 5-37 defines entries for cases involving one or two spatial layers. In the case of only one spatial layer, spatial multiplexing is obviously not possible, but there still are gains to be had from pre-coding. For the case of four transmit antennas, a correspondingly larger codebook is defined in [Ref. 7].

Note that there is a closed loop spatial multiplexing mode and an open loop spatial multiplexing mode:
I In closed loop spatial multiplexing, the base station decides on the MIMO mode and the precoding matrix to apply based on terminal feedback. The terminal regularly estimates the MIMO channel and derives the rank of the channel matrix as well as the optimum pre-

coding matrix from the given codebook. This feedback is provided to the base station by means of uplink signaling. The network may configure a subset of the codebook that the terminal is able to select from. As a special case of closed loop spatial multiplexing, transmission mode 6 as mentioned above includes the possibility to constantly use a single transmission layer only and select the optimum precoding vector based on terminal feedback (= rank 1 precoding). This technique has a beamforming effect since the precoding vector adapts the phase of each antenna element's transmission. Note that this mode is to be distinguished from beamforming in accordance with transmission mode 7. The latter does not require any feedback signaling and provides full support for adaptive beamforming algorithms.

In the case of terminals with high velocity, the quality of the feedback signaling may deteriorate. Thus, an open loop spatial multiplexing mode is also supported which is based on predefined settings for spatial multiplexing and precoding. The feedback signaling of the terminal contains the rank, but not the optimum precoding matrix (i.e. no PMI information is included). The terminal implicitly assumes transmit diversity if just one code word is transmitted by the base station (as announced by the downlink control information DCI format 2A on PDCCH). If two code words are transmitted, the terminal assumes large delay cyclic delay diversity in conjunction with spatial multiplexing. In the case of two transmit antennas, the precoding matrix is fixed (codebook index 0 in Fig. 5-37). In the case of four transmit antennas, the precoders are assigned cyclically.

As previously mentioned, the **downlink control information (DCI)** on the PDCCH conveys the MIMO mode and precoding configuration to the terminal. For example, DCI format 2 is used for closed loop spatial multiplexing and provides a downlink assignment for up to two code words including precoding information. Three or six bits are available for precoding information for two or four transmit antennas, respectively. They are interpreted differently depending on whether information for one or two transport blocks (code words) is provided.

In the case of **transmit diversity** mode, a specific precoding is used which results in a **space-frequency block coding (SFBC)** type of transmit diversity in the case of two transmit antennas and in a combination of SFBC and **frequency switched transmit diversity (FSTD)** in the case of four antennas. Only one code word can be transmitted, and each antenna transmits the same information stream but with different coding. At a certain point in time, the antenna ports transmit the same data symbols, but with different coding and on different subcarriers. Fig. 5-38 shows an example involving the two transmit antenna case where the transmit diversity specific precoding scheme is applied to two data symbols d(0) and d(1).

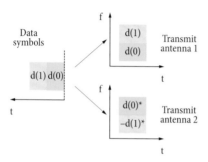

Fig. 5-38 Transmit diversity (SFBC) principle.

Beamforming

LTE defines the use of beamforming as MIMO transmission mode 7. Beamforming implies shaping the antenna radiation pattern in order to focus the transmission energy in the direction of the receiver and possibly mitigate interferers. Typically, beamforming involves an antenna array with e.g. eight antenna elements which can be individually adapted in gain and phase. The LTE standard does not prescribe how many antenna elements and which algorithms are to be used for beamforming. This is left up to implementation of the base station vendor. Instead, the LTE specifications refer to an "antenna port 5" which can be considered as a virtual antenna port that is created by the use of beamforming. From the terminal's perspective, the transmission appears to originate from this single antenna port.

Since the terminals do not know the applied beamforming weights at the base station antennas, the channel estimation in a beamforming scenario can no longer be based on common reference signals. Therefore, UE-specific reference signals are introduced in LTE. Only PDSCH transmissions can be beamformed, and the UE-specific reference signals are transmitted only on the resource blocks where this PDSCH is mapped. The terminal is informed by higher layer signaling that UE-specific reference signals shall be used as the phase reference for demodulating the PDSCH. Otherwise, the terminal would not know that it is receiving a beamformed transmission.

Since the base station is responsible for forming the beam, no terminal feedback is required. Typically, beamforming is easier to use in TDD technology where the uplink and downlink use the same frequency band and the radio channel can be considered reciprocal. Therefore, in LTE TDD mode, the feature involving UE-specific reference signals has been made mandatory for terminals to support. This feature is optional for LTE FDD terminals.

5.5.3 Reporting of terminal feedback for MIMO

In order for MIMO schemes to work properly, each terminal has to report information about the mobile radio channel characteristics to the base station. Many different reporting modes and formats are available which are dependent mainly on the MIMO transmission mode which is configured by the network.

The network can configure periodic reporting of the MIMO feedback on the PUCCH control channel. In this case, the reporting instances, periodicity, etc. are also configured by the base station. If the terminal has a PUSCH resource available, it must be used instead of PUCCH. Aperiodic reporting on the PUSCH is also possible: It is initiated via a CQI request that is contained in the uplink scheduling grant in DCI format 0. It enables the base station to explicitly request a report.

Reporting of MIMO feedback consists of the following elements:
ı The channel quality indicator (CQI) is an indication of the downlink mobile radio channel quality as experienced by the reporting terminal. Essentially, the terminal is proposing to the base station an optimum modulation scheme and coding rate to use for a given radio link quality so that the resulting transport block error rate would not exceed 10 %. There are 16 combinations of the modulation scheme and coding rate that are specified as possible CQI values. A higher CQI value stands for a higher-order modulation scheme and a higher code rate (i.e. less redundancy). The terminal may report different types of CQI. A so-called wideband CQI refers to the complete system bandwidth. Alternatively, the UE may evaluate a subband CQI

value per subband of a certain number of resource blocks which is configured by the higher layers. The full set of subbands would cover the entire system bandwidth. The MIMO mode, aperiodic or periodic reporting and the higher layer configuration determine which CQI type to report.

ı The precoding matrix indicator (PMI) is an indication of the preferred precoding matrix to be used in the base station for a given radio condition. The PMI value refers to the codebook table; (e.g. Fig. 5-37 for the two transmit antenna case for spatial multiplexing) and can represent either the full bandwidth or a certain subset of resource blocks. As before, the MIMO mode, aperiodic or periodic reporting and the higher layer configuration determine which PMI type to report. PMI reports are needed for closed loop spatial multiplexing, multi-user MIMO and closed loop spatial multiplexing with a single transmission layer (i.e. transmission modes 4, 5 and 6). However, they are not used in open loop spatial multiplexing.

ı The rank indication (RI) is the number of useful transmission layers when spatial multiplexing is used. It refers to the rank of the MIMO channel matrix. In the case of transmit diversity, the RI is equal to 1. For spatial multiplexing, the terminal shall determine an RI corresponding to the number of useful transmission layers. The RI is required only for MIMO transmission modes 3 and 4.

5.5.4 Uplink MIMO in LTE

Uplink MIMO schemes for LTE differ from downlink MIMO schemes in order to restrict terminal complexity. For the uplink, MU-MIMO can be used. Multiple user terminals may transmit simultaneously on the same resource block(s). This is also referred to as spatial division multiple access (SDMA). This scheme requires only one transmit antenna on the terminal end. The terminals sharing the same resource block must apply mutually orthogonal pilot patterns, i.e. demodulation reference signals. The base station must carefully select the MU-MIMO resources.

In order to exploit the benefits of two or more transmit antennas while still maintaining terminal costs low, transmit antenna selection can be used. In this case, the terminal has two transmit antennas but only one transmit chain and amplifier. A switch then chooses the antenna that provides the best channel to the base station. In the case of the closed loop scheme defined in LTE, this decision is made in accordance with feedback provided by the base station. The CRC parity bits for DCI format 0 are scrambled with an antenna selection mask indicating the terminal's antenna port 0 or 1. Support for transmit antenna selection is a terminal capability. If the terminal does not support the closed loop scheme, an open loop antenna selection scheme can be implemented. In this case, the decision on which transmit antenna to select is made inside the terminal and is implementation-dependent.

5.6 Radio protocol architecture

5.6.1 Overview

The base station functionality has increased significantly in LTE compared to WCDMA release 99. The major radio-related procedures are now hosted in the base station, including functions for radio bearer control, admission control, mobility control, uplink and downlink scheduling as well as measurement configuration. This is also reflected in the radio protocol architecture.

The LTE **user plane** protocol stack over the radio interface is shown in Fig. 5-39. All user plane protocol layers terminate on the terminal and base station ends, including the physical layer (PHY), medium access control (MAC), radio link control (RLC) and packet data convergence protocol (PDCP).

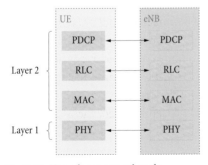

Fig. 5-39 User plane protocol stack.

Source: [3GPP TS 36.300, Ref. 4], reproduced by permission of 3GPP

The LTE **control plane** protocol stack over the radio interface is shown in Fig. 5-40. It is based on the same layer 1 and layer 2 protocols as the user plane protocol stack. In addition, the layer 3 protocols consist of radio resource control (RRC) terminating in the terminal and base station as well as non-access stratum (NAS) signaling terminating in the terminal and MME.

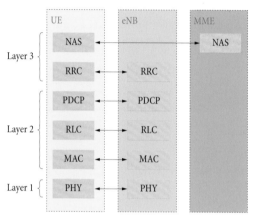

Fig. 5-40 Control plane protocol stack.

Source: [3GPP TS 36.300, Ref. 4], reproduced by permission of 3GPP

5.6.2 Layer 2 structure

Fig. 5-41 and Fig. 5-42 show the downlink and uplink structure of layer 2. The service access points between the physical layer and the MAC layer provide the **transport channels**. The service access points between the MAC and the RLC layers provide the **logical channels**. **Radio bearers** are defined on top of the PDCP layer. Multiplexing of several logical channels onto the same transport channel is possible.

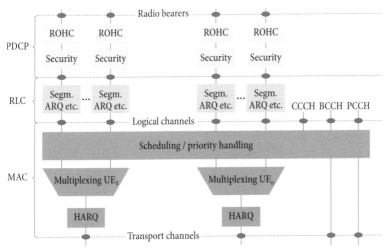

Fig. 5-41 Downlink layer 2 structure.

Source: [3GPP TS 36.300, Ref. 4], reproduced by permission of 3GPP

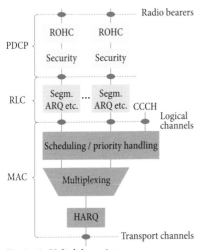

Fig. 5-42 Uplink layer 2 structure.

Source: [3GPP TS 36.300, Ref. 4], reproduced by permission of 3GPP

Transport channels

In order to reduce the complexity of the LTE protocol architecture, the number of transport channels has been reduced. This is mainly due to the focus on shared channel operation, i.e. dedicated channels are no longer used.

Downlink transport channels are:
- I Broadcast channel (BCH)
- I Downlink shared channel (DL-SCH)
- I Paging channel (PCH)

Uplink transport channels are:
- I Uplink shared channel (UL-SCH)
- I Random access channel (RACH)

Logical channels

Logical channels can be classified into control and traffic channels. Control channels are:
- I Broadcast control channel (BCCH)
- I Paging control channel (PCCH)
- I Common control channel (CCCH)
- I Dedicated control channel (DCCH)

Traffic channels are:
- I Dedicated traffic channel (DTCH)

Mapping between logical and transport channels in the downlink and uplink is illustrated in Fig. 5-43 and Fig. 5-44. Mapping from transport channels to physical channels is also illustrated.

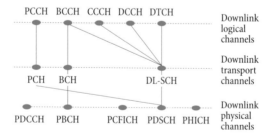

Fig. 5-43 Mapping between downlink logical and transport channels and between transport and physical channels.

Source: [3GPP TS 36.300, Ref. 4], reproduced by permission of 3GPP

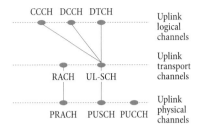

Fig. 5-44 Mapping between uplink logical and transport channels and between transport and physical channels.

Source: [3GPP TS 36.300, Ref. 4], reproduced by permission of 3GPP

Layer 2 protocols

As indicated in Fig. 5-41 and Fig. 5-42, MAC is responsible for mapping between logical and transport channels and for multiplexing / demultiplexing of data from different logical channels. It is important to note that MAC also hosts the scheduling functionality for the air interface, i.e. prioritization of traffic flows, selection of transport formats, etc. The hybrid automatic repeat request (HARQ) protocol is also located in MAC, i.e. MAC evaluates the ACK / NACK messages to schedule retransmissions or new packets. HARQ is an N-channel stop-and-wait protocol with asynchronous downlink retransmissions and synchronous uplink retransmissions; see 5.7.4, page 83.

RLC transfers upper layer protocol data units (PDUs). As transmission modes, transparent mode (only for BCCH, CCCH and PCCH logical channels), acknowledged mode (DCCH, DTCH logical channels) and unacknowledged mode (DTCH logical channel) are defined. For transmission over the radio interface in acknowledged and unacknowledged mode, RLC can perform concatenation, segmentation and reassembly of packets as well as reordering, duplicate detection and discarding of packets. In the case of acknowledged mode, an ARQ protocol is also run in the RLC layer. ARQ retransmissions are based on RLC status reports and HARQ / ARQ interaction. Unlike UMTS WCDMA, the RLC protocol in LTE can perform re-segmentation for PDUs to be retransmitted in case the retransmission would otherwise not suit the existing transmission opportunity.

PDCP functions are applicable to DCCH and DTCH logical channels. Besides the functions needed for data transfer and maintenance of PDCP sequence numbers, PDCP hosts the important security functions of ciphering and integrity protection. This is a major change compared to release 99 in which these functions were defined with a location in RLC. PDCP in LTE is also responsible for IP header compression using the **robust header compression** (ROHC) protocol.

Transport block structure (MAC protocol data unit (PDU))
MAC provides transport blocks (= MAC PDUs) to the physical layer for transmission. The structure of the MAC PDU has to take into account the LTE multiplexing options and the requirements of functions such as scheduling, timing alignment, etc.

A MAC PDU for the downlink shared channel (DL-SCH) or uplink shared channel (UL-SCH) consists of a MAC header, zero or more MAC service data units (SDU), zero or more MAC control elements and optional padding; see Fig. 5-45.

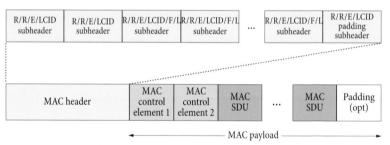

Fig. 5-45 Structure of the MAC PDU.

Source: [3GPP TS 36.321, Ref. 16], reproduced by permission of 3GPP

The MAC header may consist of multiple subheaders. Each subheader corresponds to a MAC control element, a MAC SDU or padding, and provides more information on the respective field in terms of the content and length. MAC SDUs can belong to different logical channels (indicated by the logical channel identifier (LCID) field in the subheader) so that multiplexing of logical channels is possible.

The following MAC control elements are specified which are identified by the LCID field in the MAC subheader:
ı Buffer status
ı Cell radio network temporary identifier (C-RNTI)
ı Discontinuous reception (DRX) command
ı UE contention resolution identity: This is used during random access as a means to resolve contention; see Fig. 5-47

ı Timing advance: This indicates the amount of timing adjustment the UE must apply in the uplink
ı Power headroom

Inside the physical layer, the transport block corresponds to a code word; see Fig. 5-36. This means that in the case of MIMO spatial multiplexing, up to two transport blocks corresponding to two code words can be transmitted per transmission time interval per terminal.

5.6.3 Radio resource control (RRC)

The radio resource control (RRC) protocol is responsible for handling layer 3 procedures over the air interface such as the following:
ı Broadcast of system information
ı RRC connection control, i.e. paging, establishing / reconfiguring / releasing RRC connections, assignment of UE identities, establishing / reconfiguring / releasing radio bearers
ı Initial security activation for ciphering and integrity protection
ı Mobility control, also for inter-RAT handovers
ı Quality of service control
ı Measurement configuration control

System information broadcast provides the terminal with important information about the cell, e.g. cell (re-)selection parameters, neighboring cell information and common channel configuration information. System information is divided into the *MasterInformationBlock* (MIB) message transmitted on the BCH / PBCH (see 5.4.1, page 31 and 5.7.1, page 69) and a number of *SystemInformationBlocks* (SIBs) transmitted on the DL-SCH. *SystemInformationBlockType1* message carries the scheduling information for all other system information blocks that are mapped to so-called *SystemInformation* (SI) messages and transmitted with a configurable periodicity. Fig. 5-46 shows the content of the different system information block types.

MIB: Physical layer info	SIB type 1: Access restrictions, SIB scheduling info	SIB type 2: Common and shared channel info
SIB type 3: Cell reselection info	SIB type 4: Cell reselection info, intra-fr. neighbour info	SIB type 5: Cell reselection info, inter-fr. neighbour info
SIB type 6: Cell reselection info for UTRA	SIB type 7: Cell reselection info for GERAN	SIB type 8: Cell reselection info for CDMA2000
SIB type 9: Home eNB identifier (HNBID)	SIB type 10: ETWS primary notification	SIB type 11: ETWS secondary notification

Fig. 5-46 System information block types. ETWS = Earthquake and tsunami warning system.

RRC is also responsible for lower layer configuration. The physical layer parameterization can be optimized by RRC for specific applications and scenarios and to meet quality of service requirements. Physical layer configuration includes, for example, configuration of the power setting of the PDSCH, uplink power control, PRACH resources, the sounding reference signal and much more.

RRC (and NAS) messages are transmitted via **signaling radio bearers** (SRBs). These are special radio bearers (RBs) that cannot be used for transmission of user data. More specifically, the following three SRBs are defined:

I SRB0 is for RRC messages using the CCCH logical channel
I SRB1 is for RRC messages (which may include a piggybacked NAS message) as well as for NAS messages prior to the establishment of SRB2 (all using the DCCH logical channel). SRB1 is set up during RRC connection establishment.
I SRB2 is for NAS messages using the DCCH logical channel. SRB2 has a lower priority than SRB1 and is always configured by E-UTRAN after security activation.

5.7 Radio-related procedures

5.7.1 Cell search

During the cell search, the terminal acquires time and frequency synchronization and identifies the physical layer cell identity. The first step in the cell search in LTE is based on specific synchronization signals. LTE uses a hierarchical cell search scheme similar to WCDMA. Thus, the primary synchronization signal and the secondary synchronization signal are defined. The synchronization signals are transmitted twice per 10 ms on predefined slots; see Fig. 5-22 for FDD and Fig. 5-23 for TDD. In the frequency domain, they are transmitted on 62 subcarriers within 72 reserved subcarriers around the DC subcarrier.

The 504 available physical layer cell identities are grouped into 168 physical layer cell identity groups. Each group contains three unique physical layer identities (0, 1 or 2). The secondary synchronization signal carries the physical layer cell identity group and the primary synchronization signal carries the physical layer identity 0, 1 or 2. Together, they unambiguously define the physical layer cell identity.

In the next step in accessing the cell, the physical broadcast channel (PBCH) must be read by the terminal. It carries the master information block with basic physical layer information: System bandwidth, PHICH configuration and system frame number. Additionally, the number of base station transmit antennas can be derived: The cyclic redundancy check (CRC) bits of the PBCH are scrambled with a mask identifying the base station transmit antenna configuration (1, 2 or 4 transmit antennas). The PBCH is transmitted within specific symbols (see Fig. 5-22 and Fig. 5-23) of the first subframe in a radio frame on the 72 subcarriers centered around the DC subcarrier. The PBCH has a 40 ms transmission time interval.

After having read the master information block, the terminal acquires additional system information blocks in order to be able to access the cell or identify possible access restrictions.

5.7.2 Initial access and connection setup

A contention-based random access procedure is used to request initial access. Note that the random access procedure may also be used as part of handover or to re-establish uplink synchronization. For these cases, 3GPP defines a non-contention-based **random access** procedure as well; here, the network assigns a dedicated random access preamble to the terminal. In the following, the focus is on the contention-based procedure for initial access as illustrated in Fig. 5-47.

Fig. 5-47 Random access procedure (contention-based).

Source: [3GPP TS 36.300, Ref. 4], reproduced by permission of 3GPP

In step ❶ in Fig. 5-47, the preamble is sent. The transmission of the random access preamble is restricted to certain time and frequency resources. The time-frequency resource where the preamble is sent is associated with an identifier known as the random access radio network temporary identifier (RA-RNTI). Different PRACH configurations are defined which indicate system and subframe numbers with PRACH opportunities as well as possible preamble formats. The PRACH configuration is provided by the higher layers.

In step ❷, a random access response is generated in the **medium access control (MAC)** layer of the base station and sent on the downlink shared channel. It is addressed to the terminal via the RA-RNTI and contains a timing advance value, an uplink grant and a temporary cell radio network temporary identifier (C-RNTI). Note that the base station may generate multiple random access responses for different terminals which can be concatenated within one MAC protocol data unit (PDU). The preamble identifiers associated with these random access responses are part of the MAC header of the PDU so the terminal can determine whether there exists a random access response for the used preamble.

70

In step ❸, the terminal sends an *RRCConnectionRequest* message for initial access on the uplink common control channel (CCCH) based on the uplink grant received in step ❷. This is often referred to as message 3 of the random access procedure.

In step ❹, contention resolution is completed by mirroring back in a MAC PDU the uplink CCCH service data unit (SDU) received in step 3. The message is sent on the downlink shared channel and addressed to the terminal via the temporary C-RNTI. If the received message matches the one sent in step 3, the contention resolution is considered successful. If the random access procedure was successful, the temporary C-RNTI is promoted to a C-RNTI that is used subsequently for uniquely identifying the RRC connection to the terminal and for scheduling.

After the random access procedure, the RRC connection setup procedure is completed. The terminal can then perform the registration (attach) procedure in order to receive services that require registration. The procedure typically includes authentication, UE capability enquiry, non access stratum (NAS) security, RRC security and default EPS bearer establishment. During the initial attach procedure, the mobile equipment identity is obtained from the terminal.

The overall sequence of exchanged layer 3 messages is shown in Fig. 5-48. Note that NAS messages can be piggybacked on RRC messages, e.g. the attach request is piggybacked on the RRC connection setup complete message.

The default EPS bearer may be used for user data transmission. However, if services with special quality of service requirements need to be set up, a dedicated EPS bearer must be established. This involves an RRC connection reconfiguration procedure. As an alternative to the sequence listed in Fig. 5-48, the RRC connection can be released after the attach and the default EPS bearer setup.

Note in Fig. 5-48 that security mode procedures take place both on the non access stratum (NAS) and access stratum (AS) levels. Once security is activated on the AS level, all RRC messages on signaling radio bearer 1 and 2 (SRB1 and SRB2), including those containing a NAS or a non-3GPP message, are integrity protected and ciphered by the PDCP layer. NAS independently applies integrity protection and ciphering to the NAS messages. Note that AS security is not activated during the initial phase of the RRC connection. Only upon receiving the UE context from the EPC does E-UTRAN activate security (both ciphering and integrity protection) using the initial security activation procedure.

No.	UE eNB	Message sequence	
		Layer	Message
1	←	RRC	*SystemInformation* (BCCH)
2	→	RRC	*RRCConnectionRequest*
3	←	RRC	*RRCConnectionSetup*
4	→	RRC	*RRCConnectionSetupComplete*
		NAS	ATTACH REQUEST
		NAS	PDNCONNECTIVITYREQUEST
5	←	RRC	*DLInformationTransfer*
		NAS	AUTHENTICATION REQUEST
6	→	RRC	*ULInformationTransfer*
		NAS	AUTHENTICATION RESPONSE
7	←	RRC	*DLInformationTransfer*
		NAS	SECURITY MODE COMMAND
8	→	RRC	*ULInformationTransfer*
		NAS	SECURITY MODE COMPLETE
9	←	RRC	*UECapabilityEnquiry*
10	→	RRC	*UECapabilityInformation*
11	←	RRC	*SecurityModeCommand*
12	→	RRC	*SecurityModeComplete*
13	←	RRC	*RRCConnectionReconfiguration*
		NAS	ATTACH ACCEPT
		NAS	ACTIVATE DEFAULT EPS BEARER CONTEXT REQUEST
14	→	RRC	*RRCConnectionReconfigurationComplete*
15	→	RRC	*ULInformationTransfer*
		NAS	ATTACH COMPLETE
		NAS	ACTIVATE DEFAULT EPS BEARER CONTEXT ACCEPT

Fig. 5-48 Attach and default EPS bearer setup.

5.7.3 Resource assignment

5.7.3.1 Scheduling of downlink resources

As outlined in 5.4.1, page 31, the scheduling information is conveyed via the downlink control information (DCI) on the PDCCH. This means that in the case of dynamic scheduling, the terminal reads the PDCCH in the beginning of each subframe and then, in case resources are scheduled, switches to the correct resource blocks within that same subframe. One PDCCH carries the DCI for one terminal so there can be multiple PDCCHs in a subframe. The question is: Where exactly does the terminal look for its PDCCH assignment without having to read every possible resource?

The resource elements carrying the PCFICH, PHICH and PDCCH are organized into **resource element groups**. Resource element groups consist of four consecutive resource elements (or six in the case of OFDM symbols carrying reference symbols) so they can carry quadruplets of data symbols. For the PDCCH, the resource element groups are further aggregated into so-called **control channel elements (CCEs)**. One CCE consists of nine resource element groups and each resource element group carries four PDCCH symbols. Each PDCCH is then transmitted on an aggregation of 1, 2, 4 or 8 consecutive control channel elements (CCEs). Some resource element groups already carry the PHICH and PCFICH and are therefore not available for the PDCCH. The remaining resource element groups can be assigned to CCEs for the PDCCH. Four different PDCCH formats are available; see Fig. 5-49. They differ in terms of the number of CCEs required. The base station scheduler has to select the optimum PDCCH format for a given DCI message in order to ensure the terminal can be reached reliably with reasonable PDCCH overhead.

PDCCH format	Number of CCEs	Number of resource-element groups	Number of PDCCH bits
0	1	9 = 1 CCE	72 (= 9·4 symbols·2 (QPSK))
1	2	18 = 2 CCEs	144 (= 18·4 symbols·2 (QPSK))
2	4	36 = 4 CCEs	288 (= 36·4 symbols·2 (QPSK))
3	8	72 = 8 CCEs	576 (= 72·4 symbols·2 (QPSK))

Fig. 5-49 Supported PDCCH formats.

Source: [3GPP TS 36.211, Ref. 7], reproduced by permission of 3GPP

Depending on the configured MIMO transmission mode, the terminal has to monitor only certain DCI types (e.g. DCI format 1A and DCI format 2 for transmission mode 4 / closed loop spatial multiplexing and in addition DCI format 0 for the uplink scheduling grants). Moreover, the terminal does not have to monitor every possible PDCCH per subframe, but only a set of PDCCH candidates in every regular (i.e. non-DRX) subframe. This means the terminal attempts to decode each of the PDCCHs in the set in accordance with all of the monitored DCI formats. The set of PDCCH candidates is found in a so-called search space which contains a defined number of PDCCHs. This depends on the size of the search space in CCEs and the aggregation level (equivalent to PDCCH format) 1, 2, 4 or 8. There are four UE-specific search spaces defined (aggregation level 1, 2, 4, 8) and two common search spaces for all terminals in a cell (aggregation level 4, 8) which the terminal must monitor. The terminal must look for PDCCHs in the search spaces of different aggregation levels since there is no predefined rule for mapping a certain DCI type to a certain PDCCH format. For the UE-specific search spaces, the starting position varies from subframe to subframe in accordance with a pre-defined rule. This provides more flexibility to the base station scheduler in case there is a limitation in the PDCCH positions in a certain subframe due to the allocation rules.

Type	Search space		Number of PDCCH candidates and PDCCH format	
	Aggregation level	Size in CCEs		
UE-specific	1	6	6	Format 0
	2	12	6	Format 1
	4	8	2	Format 2
	8	16	2	Format 3
Common	4	16	4	Format 2
	8	16	2	Format 3

Fig. 5-50 PDCCH candidates monitored by a UE.

Source: [3GPP TS 36.213, Ref. 15], reproduced by permission of 3GPP

The cyclic redundancy check (CRC) of each PDCCH is scrambled with a UE identity (RNTI = radio network temporary identifier) and is used for addressing the message to a specific terminal. Different RNTIs are defined for different use cases. For the regular scheduling of terminal-specific data, typically the terminal-specific cell radio network temporary identifier (C-RNTI) would be used and the terminal would look for PDCCH messages addressed to its C-RNTI in both the common and terminal-specific search space. Fig. 5-51 provides an overview of the different RNTIs and their use cases.

UE identity	Search space	DCI format	Use case
SI-RNTI	Common	1A, 1C	System information broadcast on DL-SCH
P-RNTI	Common	1A, 1C	Paging messages and system information change notification on PCH
RA-RNTI	Common	1A, 1C	Random access response
C-RNTI	Common, UE-specific	Depending on transmission mode	UE-specific dynamic scheduling of user data
SPS C-RNTI	Common, UE-specific	Depending on transmission mode	UE-specific semi-persistent scheduling (SPS) of user data
Temporary C-RNTI	Common, UE-specific by temporary C-RNTI	1, 1A	Signaling during initial access, contention resolution

Fig. 5-51 Downlink scheduling configurations.

SI-RNTI and P-RNTI have pre-defined values known to all terminals (SI-RNTI = FFFFhex, P-RNTI = FFFEhex; see [Ref. 16]).

Besides the dynamic scheduling mode in which the terminal must monitor each transmission time interval for a possibly different assignment, a semi-persistent scheduling (SPS) mode is also defined. This is especially beneficial for services with a more predictable traffic pattern consisting of frequent small packets, e. g. voice over IP. In this case, the overhead for the terminal to read and decode the PDCCHs is reduced since the terminals do not have to read the PDCCH to receive the initial transmissions of these data packets. The network can allocate semi-persistent downlink resources for the first HARQ transmissions to terminals by a semi-persistent scheduling grant, which can then be reused implicitly in the subsequent transmission time intervals in accordance with the periodicity defined by RRC (parameter *semiPersistSchedIntervalDL*). This periodicity can assume values between 10 and 640 subframes and determines how often the allocation is repeated. RRC configures all of the parameters for this semi-persistent scheduling mode as well as the number of HARQ processes for SPS mode.

The terminal recognizes a semi-persistent scheduling activation if the CRC parity bits on the PDCCH are scrambled with the SPS C-RNTI and the new data indicator field is set to "0". This activates the SPS mode. Similarly, the SPS mode can be deactivated by a predefined DCI setting. Note that the terminal still continues to monitor regular PDCCHs based on C-RNTI which may contain data packets for other services. Only if the terminal cannot find its C-RNTI on the PDCCHs does it assume continuation of the semi-persistent allocation. Otherwise, the C-RNTI based allocation overrides the semi-persistent allocation for that transmission time interval. Moreover, the terminal watches for retransmissions of semi-persistently scheduled packets based on PDCCH with SPS C-RNTI.

Since no PDCCH is available for semi-persistently scheduled packets, the PUCCH resource to use for ACK / NACK cannot be derived from the PDCCH position. Therefore, RRC configures up to four possible PUCCH resources to use for ACK / NACK. The "TPC command for PUCCH" field in the DCI for SPS activation then points to one of these resources.

There are different ways to signal the actual resource allocation for the PDSCH within DCI in order to obtain a trade-off between signaling overhead and flexibility. DCI formats 1, 2 and 2A may use resource allocation types 0 or 1 as described hereafter. The resource allocation type which is used is signaled by a resource allocation header field. The resource allocation type 2 method is specified for DCI formats 1A, 1B, 1C and 1D.

In resource allocation type 0, a bit map indicates the resource block groups that are allocated to a terminal. A resource block group (RGB) consists of a set of consecutive physical resource blocks (1 to 4 depending on the system bandwidth; see Fig. 5-52).

System bandwidth (number of resource blocks)	RBG size (P)
≤ 10	1
11–26	2
27–63	3
64–110	4

Fig. 5-52 Resource block group (RBG) size for each system bandwidth.

Source: [3GPP TS 36.213, Ref. 15], reproduced by permission of 3GPP

The resource block groups allocated to a terminal do not have to be adjacent to one other. Fig. 5-53 (left section) illustrates the definition of resource block groups for the 20 MHz bandwidth case.

In resource allocation type 1, a bitmap indicates specific physical resource blocks inside a selected resource block group subset. For a certain system bandwidth, the number of resource block group subsets corresponds to P in accordance with Fig. 5-52. Fig. 5-53 for the 20 MHz case shows the definition of P = 4 resource block group subsets along with the resource block groups which are part of each subset. The information field for the resource block assignment on the PDCCH is split into three parts: One part indicates the selected resource block group subset p. One bit indicates whether a shift shall be applied when interpreting the bitmap in view of the resource blocks. The third part contains the bitmap that indicates specific physical resource blocks inside the resource block group subset to the terminal. In consequence, the resource blocks allocated to the terminal are not adjacent to one other; instead, this terminal's resource allocation may be spread across the available bandwidth.

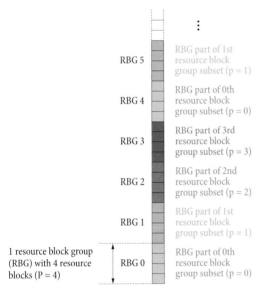

Fig. 5-53   Resource block groups for resource allocation type 0/1 (example: 20 MHz bandwidth, one resource block group contains P = 4 resource blocks).

In resource allocation type 2, physical resource blocks are not directly allocated. Instead, virtual resource blocks are allocated which are then mapped onto physical resource blocks. This can be either a localized assignment of contiguous virtual resource blocks or a distributed virtual resource block assignment. "Distributed" refers to a distribution of the resource blocks over the frequency domain based on a limited set of resource allocations that can be shared among two terminals. DCI formats 1A, 1B and 1D use a one-bit flag within DCI to discriminate the two assignment types. DCI format 1C always uses distributed assignment.

In the case of resource allocation type 2, the information field for the resource block assignment carried on the PDCCH contains a resource indication value (RIV) from which a starting virtual resource block and a length in terms of contiguously allocated virtual resource blocks can be derived.

In the localized case, there is a one-to-one mapping between virtual and physical resource blocks. The localized allocation can range between one single resource block up to the complete bandwidth.

Example: Let us assume a 10 MHz signal, i.e. 50 resource blocks are available. A terminal is to be assigned an allocation of 10 resource blocks (L_{CRBs} = 10) starting from resource block 15 (RB_{start} = 15) in the frequency domain. In accordance with the formula in [36.213, Ref. 15], a resource indication value (RIV) of 465 would then be signaled to the terminal within DCI on the PDCCH and the terminal could unambiguously derive the starting resource block and the number of allocated resource blocks from the RIV again. For the given bandwidth of 10 MHz, 11 bit are available for signaling the RIV within the DCI. Signaling L_{CRBs} and RB_{start} explicitly would require 12 bits for the 10 MHz case. By focusing on the realistic combinations of L_{CRBs} and RB_{start} using the RIV, one bit can therefore be saved and signaling made more efficient. For more examples of usage of the RIV value, see the LTE resource allocation tool in [Ref. 17].

In the distributed case of resource allocation type 2, the virtual resource block numbers are mapped to physical resource block numbers in accordance with the rule specified in [Ref. 7] and inter-slot hopping is applied: The first part of a virtual resource block pair is mapped to one physical resource block and the other part of the virtual resource block pair is mapped to a physical resource block which is a pre-defined gap distance away (which causes the inter-slot hopping). By doing so, frequency diversity is achieved. This mechanism is especially attractive for small resource block allocations since they inherently provide less frequency diversity.

5.7.3.2 Scheduling of uplink resources and frequency hopping

The base station is responsible for scheduling uplink resources on the PUSCH. Scheduling grants on the PDCCH inform the terminals about the assigned time / frequency resources and transmission formats to use. The scheduling decisions may be based on quality of service parameters, terminal buffer status, uplink channel quality measurements, terminal capabilities, etc.

As in the downlink, data is allocated in multiples of one resource block. The uplink resource block size in the frequency domain is 12 subcarriers, i. e. the same as in the downlink. However, not all integer multiples of resource blocks can be allocated due to the need for simplicity in the DFT design in the uplink signal processing. Only multiples composed of factors of 2, 3 and 5 are allowed. Unlike in the downlink, terminals are always assigned contiguous resources in the LTE uplink of 3GPP release 8. The uplink transmission time interval is 1 ms (same as downlink). By using uplink frequency hopping on the PUSCH, frequency diversity effects can be exploited and interference can be averaged.

The terminal derives the uplink resource allocation for a subframe as well as the frequency hopping information from the uplink scheduling grant that was received previously by a predefined number of subframes (e. g. four subframes in the case of regular FDD operation). Downlink control information (DCI) format 0 is used on the PDCCH to convey the uplink scheduling grant; see Fig. 5-54. DCI format 0 always uses resource allocation type 2 (see above), i. e. a starting resource block and the number of contiguously allocated resource blocks are provided by the resource block assignment.

Information type	Number of bit on PDCCH	Purpose
Flag for format 0 / format 1A differentiation	1	Indicates DCI format to UE
Hopping flag	1	Indicates whether uplink frequency hopping is used or not
Resource block assignment and hopping resource allocation	Depending on bandwidth	Indicates whether to use type 1 or type 2 frequency hopping and index of starting resource block of uplink resource allocation as well as number of contiguously allocated resource blocks
Modulation and coding scheme and redundancy version	5	Indicates modulation scheme and in conjunction with the number of allocated physical resource blocks, the transport block size. Indicates redundancy version to use
New data indicator	1	Indicates whether a new transmission shall be sent
TPC command for scheduled PUSCH	2	Transmit power control (TPC) command for adapting the transmit power on the physical uplink shared channel (PUSCH)
Cyclic shift for demodulation reference signal	3	Indicates the cyclic shift to use for deriving the uplink demodulation reference signal from the base sequence
Uplink index (TDD only)	2	Indicates the uplink subframe(s) where the scheduling grant is to be applied
Downlink assignment index (DAI, TDD only)	2	Indicates the number of downlink assignments to be considered for ACK / NACK bundling
CQI request	1	Requests the UE to send a channel quality indication (CQI)

Fig. 5-54 Content of DCI format 0 carried on PDCCH.

For dynamic scheduling of the PUSCH, the terminal is addressed via its C-RNTI. Scheduling configurations based on other identities are listed in Fig. 5-55 along with the possibility to transmit power control commands with DCI formats 3/3A on the PDCCH.

UE identity	Search space	DCI format	Use case
C-RNTI	Common, UE-specific	0	Uplink scheduling grants
SPS C-RNTI	Common, UE-specific	0	Semi-persistent uplink scheduling
Temporary C-RNTI	Common	0	Random access response grant
TPC-PUCCH-RNTI	Common	3 or 3A	Uplink power control
TPC-PUSCH-RNTI	Common	3 or 3A	Uplink power control

Fig. 5-55 Uplink scheduling configurations.

LTE supports both intra- and inter-subframe frequency hopping in the uplink. It is configured per cell by the higher layers if both intra- and inter-subframe hopping or only inter-subframe hopping is supported. In intra-subframe hopping (= inter-slot hopping), the terminal hops to another frequency allocation from one slot to another within one subframe. In inter-subframe hopping, the frequency resource allocation changes from one subframe to another.

The uplink scheduling grant in DCI format 0 contains a one-bit flag for switching hopping on or off. Moreover, the terminal is informed whether to use type 1 or type 2 frequency hopping and receives the index of the first resource block in the uplink allocation.

Type 1 hopping refers to the use of an explicit offset in the 2nd slot resource allocation. Fig. 5-56 and Fig. 5-57 show two different examples. Both examples use intra- / inter-subframe hopping based on the type 1 hopping scheme but with a different offset applied. Two subframes of a 10 MHz signal are shown. The offset between the slots is different in both figures. It is adjustable and indicated to the terminal also within the resource block assignment / hopping resource allocation field in DCI format 0.

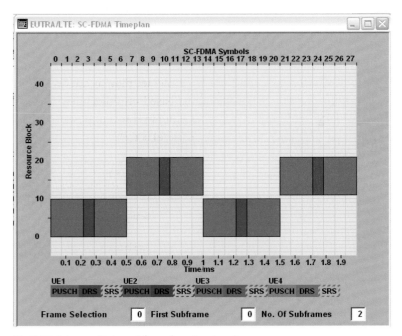

Fig. 5-56 Intra- and inter-subframe hopping, type 1.

81

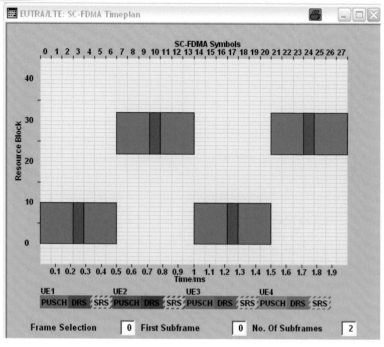

Fig. 5-57 Another example of intra- and inter-subframe hopping,
type 1, based on a different offset.

Type 2 hopping (Fig. 5-58) refers to the use of a pre-defined cell-specific hopping pattern. The bandwidth available for the PUSCH is subdivided into subbands (e.g. four subbands with five resource blocks each in the 5 MHz case) and the hopping is performed between subbands (from one slot or subframe to another depending on whether intra- or inter-subframe is configured, respectively). Note that in the case of type 2 hopping, the resource allocation for the terminal cannot be larger than the subband configured.

The terminal first determines the allocated resource blocks after applying all of the frequency hopping rules. Then, the data is mapped onto these resources, first in subcarrier order, then in symbol order.

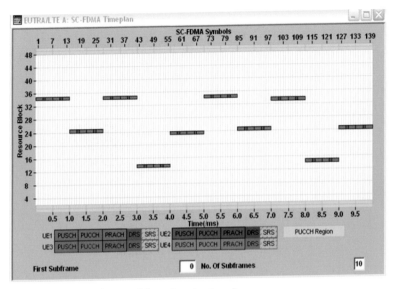

Fig. 5-58 Example of inter-subframe hopping type 2.

Semi-persistent scheduling (SPS) as explained for the downlink is also available for the uplink and configured by RRC. The terminal may use the configured SPS resource with a certain periodicity (10 ms to 640 ms, parameter *semiPersistSchedIntervalUL* configured by RRC). Activation and release of the SPS mode are executed using special settings of DCI format 0 on the PDCCH, addressed to the SPS C-RNTI. Retransmissions are either implicitly allocated (in which case the terminal uses the semi-persistent uplink allocation) or explicitly allocated via the PDCCH(s) (in which case the terminal does not follow the semi-persistent allocation). The terminal must clear the configured uplink grant immediately following a configurable number of subframes in the case of uplink inactivity (parameter *implicitReleaseAfter* configured by RRC, corresponding to 2, 3, 4 or 8 empty transmissions).

5.7.4 Hybrid ARQ

The hybrid automatic repeat request (ARQ) protocol is a retransmission protocol used to improve the robustness of data transmission. In the simple case of an ARQ protocol, the receiver is able to detect errors in received data packets and can request retransmissions. Each packet is acknowledged or negatively acknowledged: For correctly received packets, an ACK is sent back to the transmitter. For erroneous packets, a NACK is sent back to the transmitter. In the case of *hybrid* ARQ, channel coding is applied to the transmitted data packets. The receiver does not delete a packet in case the decoding fails but stores the packet in the buffer and combines it with the later retransmission. The retransmission may use the same channel coding as the initial transmission (chase combining) or use a different redundancy version (incremental redundancy).

In LTE, the hybrid ARQ protocol is used in both the uplink and downlink. Fig. 5-59 illustrates the basic principle of downlink operation.

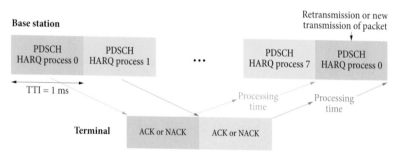

Fig. 5-59 Principle of hybrid ARQ protocol (timing not represented exactly).

In each transmission time interval of 1 ms, the base station can send a data packet on the PDSCH to the terminal. The terminal acknowledges or negatively acknowledges the packet by responding with ACK or NACK in the uplink control signaling. These ACK / NACKs are processed in the base station receiver and the base station schedules new transmissions or retransmissions accordingly. This procedure requires a certain round trip time. In a plain stop-and-wait protocol, the base station must wait for the ACK / NACK associated with each data packet before it proceeds with the next data packet or retransmission. However, in LTE (as in HSPA), this is not the case: The base station can schedule different packets in the meantime on other HARQ processes. Each HARQ process is associated with a HARQ buffer to enable storing the packet so it can be combined with later retransmissions.

LTE FDD supports up to eight downlink HARQ processes. For TDD, the maximum number of HARQ processes in the downlink depends on the UL / DL configuration; see Fig. 5-60.

TDD UL/DL configuration	Maximum number of HARQ processes
0	4
1	7
2	10
3	9
4	12
5	15
6	6

Fig. 5-60 Maximum number of downlink HARQ processes for TDD.

Source: [3GPP TS 36.213, Ref. 15], reproduced by permission of 3GPP

In the case of MIMO transmission modes with spatial multiplexing, two packets (i. e. transport blocks) can be transmitted per transmission time interval of 1 ms. They are associated with the same HARQ process. One ACK / NACK bit is sent for each transport block, i. e. they are acknowledged separately.

The uplink ACK / NACK transmission in FDD mode refers to the downlink packet that was received four subframes earlier. In TDD mode, the uplink ACK / NACK timing must again be derived from the uplink/downlink configuration.

Besides the ACK / NACK timing, there are more variations in the HARQ protocol between LTE FDD and TDD. This is due to the flexibility of different uplink-downlink configurations in TDD that necessitate special procedures. In many cases, the uplink-downlink configuration is asymmetric, thereby leading to a situation in which multiple ACK / NACKs may have to be transmitted in one single uplink subframe in order to acknowledge all of the packets that were sent in the downlink. Depending on the radio conditions for a given terminal, this may be challenging since the reliability of the ACK / NACK transmission is crucial to the overall performance. Multiple ACK / NACKs can either be multiplexed in the uplink control signaling (except for uplink-downlink configuration 5), or ACK / NACK bundling can be used. ACK / NACK bundling refers to the use of a single ACK / NACK response for multiple PDSCH transmissions. The single ACK / NACK response is created by performing a logical AND operation across all relevant ACK / NACK responses. ACK / NACK bundling and multiplexing are not supported for the FDD PDSCH acknowledgment procedure.

The uplink HARQ protocol works similarly to the downlink: The base station has the capability to request retransmissions of incorrectly received data packets. ACK / NACK information in the downlink is sent on the **physical hybrid ARQ indicator channel (PHICH)**.

For FDD, eight **HARQ processes** are supported in the uplink in regular operation. For TDD, the number of uplink HARQ processes depends on the uplink-downlink configuration; see Fig. 5-61.

TDD UL/DL configuration	Number of HARQ processes for normal HARQ operation	Number of HARQ processes for subframe bundling operation
0	7	3
1	4	2
2	2	N/A
3	3	N/A
4	2	N/A
5	1	N/A
6	6	3

Fig. 5-61 Number of synchronous UL HARQ processes for TDD.

Source: [3GPP TS 36.213, Ref. 15], reproduced by permission of 3GPP

There is another special mode defined for uplink HARQ, **subframe bundling** operation, which allows four HARQ processes for FDD only (for TDD, see Fig. 5-61). Subframe bundling can be configured by the higher layers (parameter *ttiBundling* in RRC). In the case of uplink subframe bundling, the terminal autonomously sends retransmissions with different redundancy versions in consecutive transmission time intervals (TTIs) without waiting for ACK / NACK. The ACK / NACK is awaited after this bundle of four transmission time intervals is finished. A retransmission of this TTI bundle is also a TTI bundle. For the TDD uplink, subframe bundling can be used only for uplink-downlink configurations 0, 1 and 6 as shown in Fig. 5-61.

For FDD regular operation (i.e. no subframe bundling), upon receiving a PHICH with ACK / NACK information, the terminal will adapt the PUSCH transmission four subframes later in a suitable manner, i.e. by sending a new transmission or a retransmission. For TDD, the terminal adapts the PUSCH transmission a number of subframes later depending on the uplink / downlink configuration and the signaled UL index in DCI format 0; see 5.7.3.2, page 79. The redundancy version to use in a PUSCH transmission is signaled in the uplink scheduling grant in DCI format 0.

In FDD, the terminal must look for the ACK / NACK response on the PHICH four subframes after transmission on the PUSCH (in TDD, dependent on the uplink-downlink configuration). The terminal must identify the correct PHICH group and the PHICH to use inside that group. A PHICH group consists of multiple PHICHs that are mapped to the same set of resource elements and distinguished using different orthogonal sequences. The exact PHICH resource to watch for is determined from the lowest index physical resource block of the uplink resource allocation and the uplink demodulation reference symbol cyclic shift associated with the PUSCH transmission, both indicated in the PDCCH with DCI format 0 granting the PUSCH transmission [formula in Ref. 15].

5.7.5 Power control

While downlink power control lies within the domain of the base station and is largely dependent on the base station implementation, uplink power control is clearly specified in LTE. Uplink power control is essential to limit the uplink interference level and compensate for channel fading. All uplink physical channels and signals of the terminal are subject to power control.

The setting of the terminal transmit power P_{PUSCH} for the physical uplink shared channel (PUSCH) transmission in a certain subframe i is defined by the following formula [Ref. 15]:

$$P_{PUSCH}(i) = \min\{P_{CMAX}, 10\log_{10}(M_{PUSCH}(i)) + P_{O\_PUSCH}(j) + \alpha(j) \cdot PL + \Delta_{TF}(i) + f(i)\} \, [dBm]$$

The terminal is allowed to set its configured maximum output power P_{CMAX} [Ref. 10] within certain bounds which are derived taking into account the terminal power class, possible cell-specific power limits (RRC parameter $P\text{-}Max$), possible power reductions and tolerances. It is always verified whether the transmit power calculated for a certain subframe i will be below this value P_{CMAX}. If that is the case, the power setting depends on a set of parameters:

- $M_{PUSCH}(i)$ is the number of PUSCH resource blocks assigned in subframe i.
- $P_{O\_PUSCH}(j)$ is configured by the higher layers and consists of a cell-specific component (RRC parameters *p0-NominalPUSCH* for dynamic scheduling and *p0-NominalPUSCH-Persistent* for SPS mode) and a terminal-specific component (RRC parameters *p0-UE-PUSCH* for dynamic scheduling and *p0-UE-PUSCH-Persistent* in SPS mode). The index j allows differentiation between dynamic scheduling ($j = 1$) and semi-persistent scheduling ($j = 0$).
- The parameter α is provided by the higher layers (RRC parameter *alpha*) to weight the influence of the path loss value *PL* in the formula. The path loss is measured in the terminal as PL = referenceSignalPower – higher layer filtered RSRP with the value of *referenceSignalPower* as provided by the higher layers, RSRP as the reference signal received power measurement in the terminal and the higher layer filter configuration as provided by the higher layers as well.
- The parameter $\Delta_{TF}(i)$ is needed only if configured by the higher layers (RRC parameter *deltaMCS-Enabled*). If $\Delta_{TF}(i)$ is enabled, a transport-format (TF) dependent component is considered in the power setting as well. It allows adaptation of the power in accordance with the information bit rate provided by the modulation and coding scheme used.
- $f(i)$ is the correction value derived from the transmit power control (TPC) command. The TPC commands are signaled either in DCI format 0 for a scheduled PUSCH, or signaled via DCI formats 3 or 3A (the latter using the special TPC-PUSCH-RNTI; i.e. *tpc-RNTI* configured by the higher layers). The terminal always attempts to find a PDCCH with DCI format 0 and PDCCHs with DCI format 3 or 3A in each subframe. If both are detected, the TPC information from DCI format 0 is used. DCI formats 3 and 3A allow transmission of TPC commands for several terminals, and each terminal is configured with a parameter *tpc-Index* as provided by the higher layers to identify its own command. DCI format 3 provides 2-bit power adjustments and DCI format 3A provides 1-bit power adjustments. Higher layers can additionally allow accumulation of TPC commands (RRC parameter *accumulationEnabled*), i.e. the TPC command for subframe $i - 1$ is considered as well when calculating the power adaptation for subframe i. For FDD, a TPC command is always considered

four subframes later. For TDD, this depends on the uplink-downlink configuration.

The transmit power setting for the physical uplink control channel (PUCCH) and the sounding reference symbol (SRS) obeys similar formulas. The network can, however, configure different parameter sets to provide more flexibility and take into account the nature of the different channels.

5.7.6 Timing control

The uplink timing of the terminal can be adjusted by the base station to maintain orthogonality in the uplink, i.e. to make sure that transmissions from terminals at different distances from the base station arrive at the base station receiver with proper time alignment. The timing advance command is sent as a control element in the medium access control (MAC) protocol; see Fig. 5-45 for the MAC PDU structure. As soon as a timing advance is received by the terminal, the *timeAlignmentTimer* (500 ms, 750 ms, 1280 ms, ... , 10140 ms, infinity) as provided by RRC is started or restarted. This controls how long the terminal is considered to exhibit uplink time alignment. If the terminal does not receive a new timing advance command within the duration of the timer, it must stop its uplink transmission in order to avoid interference problems.

The timing advance command indicates the change in the uplink timing (advancing or delaying the uplink transmission) relative to the current uplink timing in multiples of $16 \cdot T_s = 0.52$ µs. The timing advance command shall be applied six subframes after its reception.

5.7.7 Mobility

5.7.7.1 Intra-LTE mobility

The radio resource control (RRC) protocol in the base station is responsible for controlling mobility within LTE and between LTE and other technologies. The handover algorithms in the base station are implementation-specific, but a handover decision will typically be based upon radio measurements for the serving cell and neighboring cells and the traffic situation within the cell. Towards this end, the base station can configure the type and amount of measurement reporting. Within LTE, the RRC connection reconfiguration procedure is used to invoke a handover; see Fig. 5-62.

Fig. 5-62 RRC connection reconfiguration procedure, successful case.

Source: [3GPP TS 36.331, Ref. 18], reproduced by permission of 3GPP

The *RRCConnectionReconfiguration* message allows reconfiguration of all relevant radio parameters in order to inform the terminal about the new cell's radio configuration and possible changes in the radio bearer configuration to use after the handover.

Of course, the handover procedure affects more than just the radio network. The core network entities are also involved. This is illustrated in Fig. 5-63 based on the example of an inter-eNB, intra-MME handover. This means that the source cell and target cell belong to different base stations but to the same mobility management entity (MME).

Based on the measurement reports from the terminal, the source base station decides on a handover. It will then initiate a handover request procedure towards the target base station. This communication is executed via the X2 interface between the base stations and contains information needed by the target base station for admission control. If the target base station acknowledges the request, the source base station can start the RRC reconfiguration procedure over the air interface. The HANDOVER REQUEST ACKNOWLEDGE message over the X2 interface includes information on the new C-RNTI, target base station security parameters, etc. which is passed on within the *RRCReconfigurationRequest* message to the terminal.

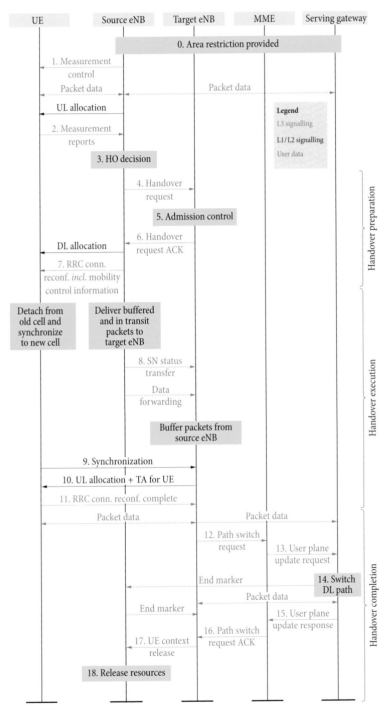

Fig. 5-63 Intra-MME handover.

Source: [3GPP TS 36.300, Ref. 4], reproduced by permission of 3GPP

Upon reception of this message, the terminal detaches from the source cell and synchronizes to the new cell. This is executed via a **random access** based procedure which is either contention-free using a dedicated RACH preamble or contention-based as in initial access. Data packets that arrive from the core network at the source base station may be forwarded via the X2 interface to the target base station which buffers the received packets. The radio bearer parameters and the sensitivity of the service to data loss determine whether data forwarding is applied or not.

As soon as the RRC reconfiguration procedure is completed at the target base station end, data packets can begin to be exchanged over the air interface and the target base station can initiate a path switch request procedure towards the MME which, in turn, invokes the user plane update request procedure towards the serving gateway. If these procedures are acknowledged, the target base station can tell the source base station to release the UE context and the resources. The handover is then successfully completed.

5.7.7.2 Mobility between LTE and other radio access technologies

In the early deployment phase, LTE coverage will likely be restricted to certain areas such as major cities and hot spots. In order to provide seamless service continuity, ensured mobility between LTE and legacy technologies is therefore essential. These legacy technologies include GSM/EDGE, WCDMA/HSPA and the CDMA2000® based technologies 1xRTT and **High Rate Packet Data (HRPD)**. Fig. 5-64 and Fig. 5-65 illustrate the mobility support between these technologies and LTE along with the procedures used to move between them. Fig. 5-64 shows the four different RRC protocol states for UMTS on the left hand side, the two different RRC protocol states for LTE in the middle and the GSM/GPRS states on the right hand side. Handovers are possible between the E-UTRA RRC CONNECTED and UMTS CELL_DCH states and between the E-UTRA RRC CONNECTED and GSM_Connected or GPRS packet transfer mode states. Additionally, cell reselection or cell change order (CCO) is possible as indicated. Fig. 5-65 shows the two different 1xRTT states on the left hand side, the two different RRC protocol states for LTE in the middle and the two different HRPD states on the right hand side. Handover is possible from E-UTRA RRC CONNECTED to 1xRTT CS Active and to HRPD Active.

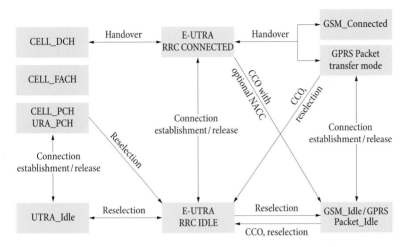

Fig. 5-64 E-UTRA states and inter RAT mobility procedures (CCO = cell change order, NACC = network assisted cell change).

Source: [3GPP TS 36.331, Ref. 18], reproduced by permission of 3GPP

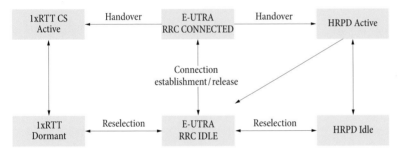

Fig. 5-65 Mobility procedures between E-UTRA and CDMA2000® based technologies (HRPD = high rate packet data).

Source: [3GPP TS 36.331, Ref. 18], reproduced by permission of 3GPP

Additionally, there is support for connection release with redirection information from E-UTRA RRC_CONNECTED to GERAN, UTRAN and CDMA2000® (HRPD idle / 1xRTT dormant mode).

As a basic mechanism to prepare and execute the handovers, radio-related information can be exchanged in transparent containers between the technologies so the source base station does not need to be aware of the target system's radio protocols.

Handover from LTE to another radio access technology (RAT) is executed via the *MobilityFromEUTRACommand* message; see Fig. 5-66. It is applicable to inter-RAT handovers to GSM / EDGE, WCDMA / HSPA and CDMA2000® systems. In the case of GSM / EDGE, the cell change order is also executed via this procedure.

Fig. 5-66 Mobility from E-UTRA, successful.

Source: [3GPP TS 36.331, Ref. 18], reproduced by permission of 3GPP

If the procedure is not successful, the terminal falls back to LTE and an RRC connection re-establishment procedure is attempted.

The opposite direction, i.e. handover to E-UTRA procedure, is executed via the RRC reconfiguration procedure as before. The *RRCConnectionReconfiguration* message is then composed in the target RAT LTE and passed on in a transparent container message to the terminal.

5.8 UE capabilities

Many LTE features are optional for the terminal to support. They are defined as a UE capability in order not to mandate the implementation of a certain feature in all sorts of terminals. TS 36.306 [Ref. 19] specifies the UE radio access capabilities. This includes the RF and inter-RAT parameters, i.e. which frequency bands and radio access technologies (RATs) a terminal supports. Furthermore, different UE categories are defined for LTE which are associated with a certain peak data rate. The categories for the downlink and uplink are shown in Fig. 5-67 and Fig. 5-68, respectively. Higher categories imply a higher implementation complexity and are typically characterized by a more complex MIMO scheme with more antennas and / or by a higher data processing and memory capability.

UE category	Maximum number of DL-SCH transport block bits received within a TTI	Maximum number of bits of a DL-SCH transport block received within a TTI	Total number of soft channel bits	Maximum number of supported layers for spatial multiplexing in DL	Maximum data rate in Mbps
Category 1	10296	10296	250368	1	10
Category 2	51024	51024	1237248	2	51
Category 3	102048	75376	1237248	2	102
Category 4	150752	75376	1827072	2	151
Category 5	299552	149776	3667200	4	300

Fig. 5-67 Downlink UE categories.

Source: [3GPP TS 36.306, Ref. 19], reproduced by permission of 3GPP

UE category	Maximum number of bits of an UL-SCH transport block transmitted within a TTI	Support for 64QAM in UL	Maximum data rate in Mbps
Category 1	5160	No	5
Category 2	25456	No	25
Category 3	51024	No	51
Category 4	51024	No	51
Category 5	75376	Yes	75

Fig. 5-68 Uplink UE categories.

Source: [3GPP TS 36.306, Ref. 19], reproduced by permission of 3GPP

The downlink UE categories differ in the maximum number of DL-SCH transport block bits and bits on one transport block received within a transmission time interval of 1 ms, in the soft buffer size for the HARQ protocol and in the number of spatial layers supported for MIMO. The uplink UE categories differ in the maximum number of UL-SCH transport block bits transmitted in one transmission time interval and in the support for the 64QAM modulation scheme.

Fig. 5-67 and Fig. 5-68 also show the maximum data rates that are achievable with a certain UE category. Please note that these maximum data rates are to be understood as theoretical peak values which cannot be delivered under realistic network conditions since they do not take into account realistic cell load and scheduling scenarios and overheads due to redundancy and signaling.

Independent from the UE category, the following features are defined as UE capabilities in [Ref. 19]:

I Supported robust header compression (ROHC) profiles

I Maximum number of header compression context sessions supported by the terminal

I Support for uplink transmit antenna selection

I Support for UE-specific reference signals for FDD

I Need for measurement gaps for inter-frequency or inter-RAT measurements

I Support for radio access technologies and radio frequency bands

6   LTE test and measurement requirements

6.1   Overview

As discussed in previous chapters, LTE is based on a variety of new techniques and characteristics: New multiple access schemes, scalable bandwidth up to 20 MHz, MIMO multi antenna technology, highly flexible resource allocation schemes and optimized control channel design, to name only a few examples. One of the design goals of LTE was to make this technology suitable for different deployment scenarios. This is why such a large number of options and configuration possibilities have found their way into the standard. Manufacturers and network operators have much room to tune LTE to suit their needs. This degree of flexibility represents an opportunity and challenge at the same time: The complexity of LTE handsets and infrastructure is significantly increased. This is in addition to the trend toward multimode and multi-RAT handsets supporting different frequency bands and cellular and wireless technologies and in addition to the increasing demand for smart phones with power-hungry multimedia applications.

First, LTE-only terminals have come up in the very initial phase of commercialization, e. g. as data cards. But soon afterwards, terminals supporting LTE plus at least one of the legacy technologies GSM / EDGE, WCDMA / HSPA and CDMA2000® 1xRTT / 1x-EV-DO or combinations thereof will be provided. This is essential in order to enable a seamless mobility experience, taking into account that LTE will not have nationwide coverage for many years to come. The need for dual mode FDD / TDD terminals represents another trend as well.

In view of this background, highly efficient test and measurement approaches are important when developing and manufacturing LTE products with excellent quality in order to fulfill the high expectations on the part of industry and subscribers. Close co-operation between test and measurement manufacturers and terminal / infrastructure manufacturers is crucial to align the development processes of LTE products and test equipment. Research and development of LTE products had begun long before the standards were finalized in 2009. Close alignment has therefore been necessary to ensure that the test equipment supports the features needed most urgently for testing the products and that the implementation baseline matches.

Manufacturers of RF components and transceivers were among the first in the industry to require test and measurement equipment supporting the new LTE standard in order to advance the development of chipsets, terminals and base stations. In this field, signal generators and analyzers are typically used for testing devices; see Fig. 6-1 and Fig. 6-2.

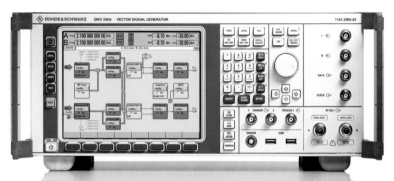

Fig. 6-1   The R&S®SMU 200 A is part of the Rohde & Schwarz family of signal generators.

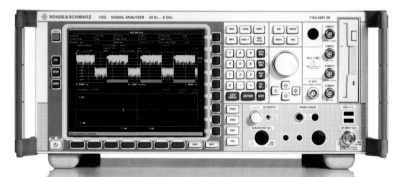

Fig. 6-2   The R&S®FSQ is part of the Rohde & Schwarz family of signal and spectrum analyzers.

Signal generators allow creation of almost any arbitrary LTE signals in accordance with the 3GPP standard. The user can select the desired settings for the frequency, power level, bandwidth, resource allocation, data formats and much more. With such a signal, receivers can be tested and RF components can be verified. To test under realistic conditions, noise can be added to the signal and propagation conditions such as multipath fading can be emulated.

Signal analyzers allow a multitude of RF measurements on LTE signals for evaluating the quality of LTE transmitters and components. This includes measurements of power, spectrum and modulation quality and verification of LTE physical channel characteristics.

Besides the technical core specifications, 3GPP working groups are responsible for defining test specifications. These are the baseline for conformance tests, but in industry they are often used as important guidelines for R&D test plans as well. Chapters 6.2, page 101 and 6.3, page 137 provide an overview of terminal and base station RF testing in accordance with 3GPP specifications.

Testing of MIMO functionality represents a special challenge for LTE. Chapter 6.4, page 161 will therefore provide more insight into the details of MIMO including discussion of channel models used to test MIMO implementations under realistic conditions.

Tests with signal generators and analyzers are non-signaling tests. Signaling is needed for the verification of radio procedures that involve downlink and uplink interaction. Radio communication testers (Fig. 6-3) are used for testing terminals including full signaling. They simulate the base station and even parts of the core network and can be used for all stages of terminal testing ranging from RF testing through full protocol testing. Chapter 6.5, page 170 will provide more details on protocol tests for terminals.

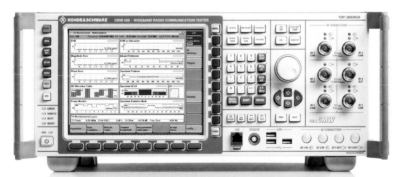

Fig. 6-3 The R&S®CMW500 wideband radio communication tester for all stages of terminal testing.

Besides testing via the RF interface, testing via the digital IQ interface has become increasingly important. Today's signal generators, analyzers and radio communication testers provide such functionality. This allows engineers to test early prototypes in which the RF section has not yet been integrated, or to test baseband and RF sections independently of one another. Besides customer-specific digital IQ interface specifications, the standards DigRF^{SM} [Ref. 20] and CPRI™ (Common Public Radio Interface, [Ref. 21]) have become well-known. DigRF defines the digital interface between baseband and RF chips on the terminal end. CPRI defines the interface between the radio equipment control (REC) and radio equipment (RE) on the base station end.

Similar to the case of GSM and UMTS, terminals will undergo special conformance tests and certification. This process will be discussed in more detail in 6.6, page 173. Fig. 6-4 shows a test system that is used for performing RF conformance tests on terminals.

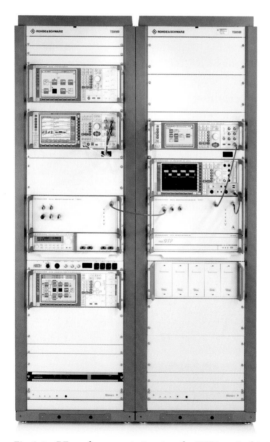

Fig. 6-4 RF conformance test system for LTE terminal test.

For deploying and optimizing LTE networks, network operators require special test and measurement solutions, e.g. in order to perform coverage measurements in the network, adjust the parameterization of network settings and evaluate the end-to-end performance. This is detailed in 6.7, page 175 and concludes the overview of LTE test and measurement.

Note that certain other important testing areas for LTE products are not covered in this book such as audio testing, application enabler testing and tests in the areas of electromagnetic compatibility (EMC) and electromagnetic interference (EMI).

6.2 Terminal RF testing

Development of RF front-ends for LTE terminals involves specific challenges. This is due to factors such as the OFDMA / SC-FDMA based radio interface, higher transmission bandwidths up to 20 MHz, higher-order modulation schemes up to 64QAM and MIMO technology. 3GPP Technical Specification 36.521 [Ref. 22] describes RF conformance tests that LTE terminals must comply with. The specification is based on the RF requirements for LTE terminals captured in 3GPP TS 36.101 [Ref. 10] which are referred to as minimum requirements. Minimum requirements do not take into account uncertainties introduced by the testing process and therefore can be understood as system or core requirements. 3GPP TS 36.521 [Ref. 22] specifies test requirements additionally that take the maximum acceptable test tolerance into account. The following chapters provide an overview of RF conformance tests for LTE terminals including transmitter, receiver and performance tests. Whenever it is useful, the chapter of the relevant specification [Ref. 22] to which a certain paragraph refers is indicated.

6.2.1 Transmitter characteristics

Fig. 6-5 provides an overview of the transmitter tests specified in 3GPP TS 36.521 [Ref. 22].

- **Transmit power:** UE maximum output power, maximum power reduction, additional maximum power reduction, configured UE transmitted output power
- **Output power dynamics:** Minimum output power, transmit OFF power, ON/OFF time mask, power control
- **Transmit signal quality:** Frequency error, error vector magnitude (EVM), carrier leakage, in-band emissions for non allocated resource blocks, EVM equalizer spectrum flatness
- **Output RF spectrum emissions:** Occupied bandwidth, spectrum emission mask, adjacent channel leakage power ratio (ACLR), spurious emissions
- **Transmit intermodulation**

Fig. 6-5   LTE terminal transmitter tests.

The test conditions for all of these tests are clearly specified. Each test case is performed for every operating band supported by the terminal and repeated for different parameterizations, e.g. in terms of bandwidth and resource allocation. The transmitter characteristics are measured on specified uplink reference measurement channels which provide predefined configurations in terms of the bandwidth and PUSCH resources. Uplink reference measurement channels are specified for different modulation schemes, bandwidth allocations and full or partial resource block allocation. Fig. 6-6 shows an example for FDD, 16QAM and full resource block allocation for all bandwidth scenarios.

Parameter	Unit	Value					
Channel bandwidth	MHz	1.4	3	5	10	15	20
Allocated resource blocks		6	15	25	50	75	100
DFT-OFDM symbols per subframe		12	12	12	12	12	12
Modulation		16QAM	16QAM	16QAM	16QAM	16QAM	16QAM
Target coding rate		3/4	1/2	1/3	3/4	1/2	1/3
Payload size	bit	2600	4264	4968	21384	21384	19848
Transport block CRC	bit	24	24	24	24	24	24
Number of code blocks per subframe*		1	1	1	4	4	4
Total number of bits per subframe	bit	3456	8640	14400	28800	43200	57600
Total symbols per subframe		864	2160	3600	7200	10800	14400
UE category		1 to 5	1 to 5	1 to 5	2 to 5	2 to 5	2 to 5

* If more than one code block is present, an additional CRC sequence of L = 24 bits is attached to each code block (otherwise L = 0 bit)

Fig. 6-6   FDD reference channels for 16QAM with full RB allocation, different bandwidths.

Source: [3GPP TS 36.521, Ref. 22], reproduced by permission of 3GPP

Fig. 6-7 shows the definition for FDD, 20 MHz bandwidth, QPSK allocation and partial resource block allocation. In the case of partial allocation, different resource allocation scenarios are covered, including one single resource block allocated at one edge of the bandwidth and varying numbers of allocated resource blocks. Note that each reference measurement channel also stipulates the coding chain parameters, i.e. the target coding rate, payload size, cyclic redundancy check (CRC) sizes, number of code blocks and resulting bits per subframe.

Parameter	Unit	Value					
Channel bandwidth	MHz	20	20	20	20	20	20
Allocated resource blocks		1	2	5	6	8	10
DFT-OFDM symbols per subframe		12	12	12	12	12	12
Modulation		QPSK	QPSK	QPSK	QPSK	QPSK	QPSK
Target coding rate		1/3	1/3	1/3	1/3	1/3	1/3
Payload size	bit	72	176	424	600	808	872
Transport block CRC	bit	24	24	24	24	24	24
Number of code blocks per subframe*		1	1	1	1	1	1
Total number of bits per subframe	bit	288	576	1440	1728	2304	2880
Total symbols per subframe		144	288	720	864	1152	1440
UE category		1 to 5	1 to 5	1 to 5	1 to 5	1 to 5	1 to 5

* If more than one code block is present, an additional CRC sequence of L = 24 bit is attached to each code block (otherwise L = 0 bit)

Parameter	Unit	Value					
Channel bandwidth	MHz	20	20	20	20	20	20
Allocated resource blocks		18	24	25	48	50	75
DFT-OFDM symbols per subframe		12	12	12	12	12	12
Modulation		QPSK	QPSK	QPSK	QPSK	QPSK	QPSK
Target coding rate		1/3	1/3	1/3	1/3	1/3	1/5
Payload size	bit	1864	2472	2216	4264	5160	4392
Transport block CRC	bit	24	24	24	24	24	24
Number of code blocks per subframe*		1	1	1	1	1	1
Total number of bits per subframe	bit	5184	6912	7200	13824	14400	21600
Total symbols per subframe		2592	3456	3600	6912	7200	10800
UE category		1 to 5	1 to 5	1 to 5	1 to 5	1 to 5	1 to 5

* If more than one code block is present, an additional CRC sequence of L = 24 bit is attached to each code block (otherwise L = 0 bit)

Fig. 6-7   FDD reference channels for 20 MHz QPSK with partial RB allocation.

Source: [3GPP TS 36.521, Ref. 22], reproduced by permission of 3GPP

The corresponding uplink reference measurement channels for TDD are defined assuming uplink-downlink configuration 1, i.e. a 2:2 ratio of downlink:uplink.

The definition of the reference measurement channels for the transmitter test (and for the other test areas of receiver test and performance test) was carefully selected by 3GPP in order to ensure the relevance of the test and its conditions on the one hand, but also to reasonably limit the overall amount of conformance testing on the other hand. Thus, terminal manufacturers may provide additional test scenarios in their individual test plans in order to verify terminal performance e.g. for measurement channels beyond those specified by 3GPP or to take into account dynamic resource allocation scenarios and other parameter settings relevant in real network operation.

6.2.1.1 Transmit power

UE maximum output power (test 6.2.2)

Terminal transmit power is an important characteristic for ensuring proper operation in the network and avoiding interference. One UE power class 3 is specified for LTE, which is equivalent to 23 dBm maximum output power plus/minus tolerance (defined as mean power in the channel bandwidth measured over one subframe). Efficient power amplifier design is crucial for the terminal, especially for conserving battery power. However, the terminal will have to transmit LTE signals with many different configurations in terms of the channel bandwidth, resource block allocation and modulation scheme. Therefore, in some uplink transmission scenarios especially with large resource block (RB) allocations, the power amplifier may not be able to operate in the linear zone.

Maximum power reduction – MPR (test 6.2.3)

In order to avoid negative impact on out-of-band emissions such as the adjacent channel leakage, a reduction in the maximum output power is allowed for these uplink signal configurations. This maximum power reduction of up to 1 or 2 dB is shown in Fig. 6-8 for UE power class 3.

Modulation	Channel bandwidth / Transmission bandwidth configuration (RB)						MPR (dB)
	1.4 MHz	3.0 MHz	5 MHz	10 MHz	15 MHz	20 MHz	
QPSK	> 5	> 4	> 8	> 12	> 16	> 18	≤ 1
16QAM	≤ 5	≤ 4	≤ 8	≤ 12	≤ 16	≤ 18	≤ 1
16QAM	> 5	> 4	> 8	> 12	> 16	> 18	≤ 2

Fig. 6-8 Maximum power reduction (MPR) for power class 3, minimum requirement.
Source: [3GPP TS 36.521, Ref. 22], reproduced by permission of 3GPP

Additional maximum power reduction (test 6.2.4)

Note that an additional maximum power reduction (A-MPR) can be applied in case the network has configured more stringent requirements for output RF spectrum emissions, e.g. due to regulatory or deployment reasons. The network indicates this using higher layer signaling (RRC parameter *AdditionalSpectrumEmission* (1 to 32) in *SystemInformationBlockType2*) to the terminals which then must comply with the more stringent requirements. In order to meet these additional requirements, the additional maximum power reduction is allowed.

Configured UE transmitted output power (test 6.2.5)

Furthermore, the network has the possibility to additionally restrict the terminal's maximum transmit power by dedicated signaling or by system information broadcast (RRC parameter *P-Max*). The test configured UE transmitted output power verifies that the terminal sets its maximum output power within the specified limits. These limits take into account the signaled value *P-Max*, the UE power class plus possible power reductions as explained above and tolerances. The test is repeated for three different signaled values of *P-Max*.

6.2.1.2 Output power dynamics

Minimum output power (test 6.3.2)

The minimum output power of the terminal shall not exceed a value of −40 dBm (mean power in one subframe) for all channel bandwidths. For UE power class 3, the specified power range is therefore −40 dBm to +23 dBm. The test on minimum output power ensures that the terminal can maintain the minimum value of the output power, e.g. to facilitate uplink interference management and avoid uplink noise rise (so-called rise over thermal) increase.

Transmit OFF power (test 6.3.3)

Testing of the transmit OFF power has a similar motivation. This test shall ensure that the terminal is not exceeding a power value of −50 dBm when the transmitter is OFF, e.g. when the terminal is not transmitting in a subframe.

ON/OFF time mask

The ON/OFF time mask provides the requirements for power ramps when the terminal switches between OFF power and ON power and vice versa. These ON/OFF switches happen, for example, when the terminal starts or ends a transmission.

General ON / OFF time mask (test 6.3.4.1)

Fig. 6-9 shows the general ON/OFF time mask for these cases. The test provides requirements for ON power and OFF power values. The transient periods needed for switching are excluded from the evaluation of the requirement.

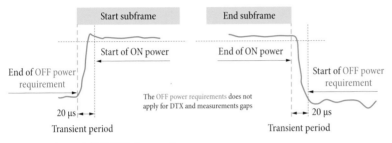

Fig. 6-9 General ON/OFF time mask.

Source: [3GPP TS 36.521, Ref. 22], reproduced by permission of 3GPP

PRACH time mask (test 6.3.4.2.1) / SRS time mask (test 6.3.4.2.2)

For OFF/ON switches caused by random access preamble (PRACH) or sounding reference symbol (SRS) transmissions, an extra PRACH and SRS time mask is defined.

Power control

As explained in 5.7.5, page 87, uplink power control is an essential technique in LTE to limit the uplink interference level and control each terminal's transmit power. Different subtests are defined for power control in [Ref. 22]. The first test on **absolute power tolerance (test 6.3.5.1)** verifies the ability of the terminal transmitter to set the initial output power on the PUSCH in the first subframe of a transmission to a specific value. The test on **relative power tolerance (test 6.3.5.2)** verifies the ability of the terminal transmitter to correctly set its output power in a subframe relative to a previous subframe. By using different test patterns, the proper handling of transmit power control (TPC) commands as well as correct power setting for changing resource allocation patterns is tested. Different resulting power step sizes are addressed. Finally, the test on **aggregate power control tolerance (test 6.3.5.3)** verifies the ability of the terminal to maintain its power level for the PUCCH and PUSCH in non-contiguous transmission within 21 ms when no power control parameters have been changed between transmissions and the TPC commands have not indicated a change in power.

6.2.1.3 Transmit signal quality

Frequency error (test 6.5.1)

The frequency setting in the terminal is derived from the signal received in the downlink. As a minimum requirement for the frequency error, the uplink modulated carrier frequency shall be accurate to within ±0.1 ppm observed over a period of one time slot, compared to the carrier frequency received from the base station.

Error vector magnitude – EVM (test 6.2.5.1)

The error vector magnitude is a measure of the modulation quality. This is a well-known measurement (e.g. from WCDMA) and it is important in LTE too. Due to the higher-order modulation schemes, stringent EVM requirements for the transmitter side apply in order to prevent a possible decrease in throughput. The error vector magnitude is a measure of the difference between a reference waveform and the measured waveform. This difference is called the error vector and its magnitude is typically given in % in 3GPP specifications. EVM is evaluated for the PUSCH, the uplink demodulation reference signal, the PUCCH and the PRACH preamble. The PUSCH EVM (and the EVM for the demodulation reference signal) shall not exceed 17.5 % for QPSK and BPSK and shall not exceed 12.5 % for 16QAM. The requirement for 64QAM has not been specified by 3GPP release 8. For the PUCCH and PRACH, the requirement is 17.5 %.

For verifying a terminal's EVM performance, test instruments for LTE typically offer a variety of EVM measurements that can even exceed the requirements of the 3GPP standard. EVM can be determined vs. subcarrier in the frequency domain or vs. time (symbols or subframes) and for particular allocations and physical channels. Fig. 6-10 and Fig. 6-11 show examples of EVM measurements taken with a signal analyzer and with a wideband radio communication tester. Fig. 6-10 shows an EVM vs. subcarrier measurement for an LTE FDD uplink signal with a 10 MHz bandwidth. The terminal transmits on 30 resource blocks so the EVM is evaluated only on this part of the bandwidth. The minimum, average and maximum values are shown in different colors. Fig. 6-11 shows the EVM vs. SC-FDMA symbols for a sample FDD uplink signal in 10 MHz bandwidth operation. One slot with 7 SC-FDMA symbols (normal cyclic prefix) is evaluated. The EVM values (current, average, maximum) for each symbol numbered from 0 to 6 are indicated.

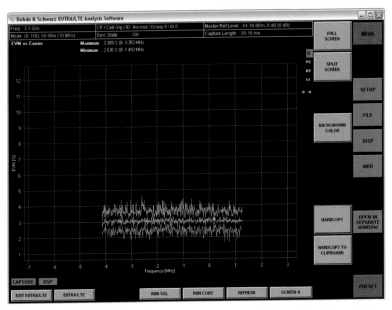

Fig. 6-10 EVM vs. subcarrier measurement on an LTE uplink signal (performed with a signal analyzer).

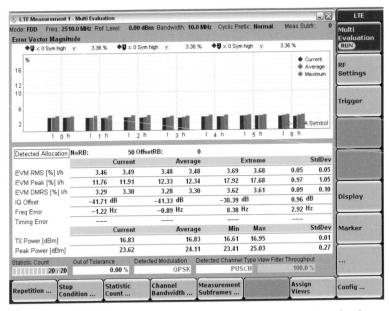

Fig. 6-11 EVM vs. symbol measurement on an LTE uplink signal (performed with a radio communication tester).

As an additional feature for verifying the implementation in detail, an EVM_{low} (l) and an EVM_{high} (h) value is shown for each symbol depending on the timing selected for the EVM measurement, i.e. the selection of the position in time for the FFT operation. In an ideal signal, the FFT could start at any instant within the cyclic prefix of a symbol without causing an error. However, in practical systems, this time window is reduced, e.g. due to time-domain windowing on the transmitter side for optimizing the out-of-band performance. EVM_{low} and EVM_{high} are determined in an intermediate step when following the EVM algorithm provided by [Ref. 22]. If EVM_{low} and EVM_{high} are significantly different, this may indicate a possible implementation issue in the time-domain windowing. The final EVM requirement is verified against the higher one of the values EVM_{low} or EVM_{high}, each averaged over 20 consecutive uplink time slots (excluding UpPTS in the case of TDD).

Carrier leakage (test 6.5.2.2)

Carrier leakage or IQ (origin) offset is another criterion for modulation quality. It can be caused by local oscillator (LO) leakage. It appears as an unmodulated sine wave at the carrier frequency and causes interference especially to the center subcarriers of the uplink signal. Fig. 6-12 shows a spectrum measurement on a signal with a clearly visible IQ origin offset. In the LTE uplink, the subcarriers are shifted by 7.5 kHz (half of the 15 kHz subcarrier spacing) towards the DC subcarrier.

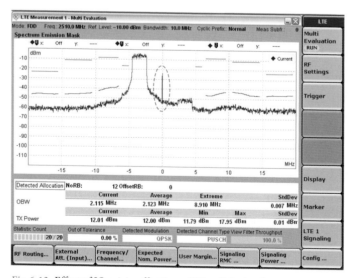

Fig. 6-12 Effect of IQ origin offset in an LTE uplink signal.

The two subcarriers close to the DC subcarrier are most affected by interference due to carrier leakage. Fig. 6-13 illustrates this frequency shifting in more detail.

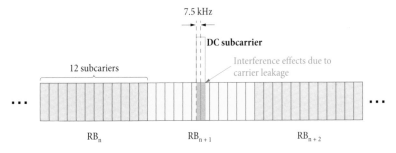

Fig. 6-13 Frequency shift of 7.5 kHz vs. DC subcarrier in the uplink.

The test requirements for the relative carrier leakage ratio are listed in Fig. 6-14 as a function of the output power range. The relative carrier leakage ratio is defined as the power ratio of the additive sinusoidal waveform and the modulated waveform.

LO leakage	
Parameters	Relative limit (dBc)
Output power > 0 dBm	−25
−30 dBm ≤ Output power ≤ 0 dBm	−20
−40 dBm ≤ Output power < −30 dBm	−10

Fig. 6-14 Minimum requirements for relative carrier leakage power.

Source: [3GPP TS 36.521, Ref. 22], reproduced by permission of 3GPP

In-band emissions for non-allocated resource blocks (test 6.5.2.3)

The in-band emissions for non-allocated resource blocks (RBs) are a measure of the interference falling into the non-allocated resource blocks caused by the allocated resource blocks. See Fig. 6-15 for an example.

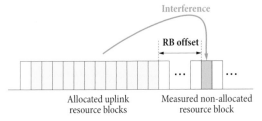

Fig. 6-15 In-band emissions for non-allocated resource blocks.

The in-band emission is evaluated in a resource block that is separated by a defined resource block offset from the allocated resource blocks. It is measured as the ratio of the terminal output power in the non-allocated resource block to the terminal output power in an allocated resource block.

Fig. 6-16 shows an example of a measurement performed with a radio communication tester. There are 12 resource blocks that are allocated at the lower part of the 10 MHz bandwidth. The measurement (blue curve) is made in subframe 0. The red curve represents the limit line provided by [Ref. 22]. Note that the limit varies depending on the resource block index. Special requirements apply for the resource blocks including the LO frequency and those including the image frequencies of an allocation.

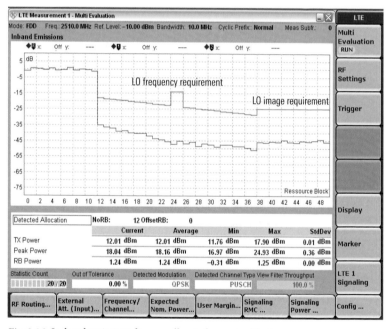

Fig. 6-16 In-band emissions for non-allocated resource blocks.

EVM equalizer spectrum flatness (test 6.5.2.4)

EVM equalizer spectrum flatness is a measure of the maximum ripple of the equalizer coefficients generated by the EVM measurement process for the allocated uplink resource blocks (Note that the definition of this requirement was modified in 3GPP TS 36.101 in March 2010 [Ref. 10] and has been aligned in a later version of 3GPP TS 36.521).

Since the EVM measurement is performed on an equalized signal, it is important to verify the spectrum flatness of the signal before equalization, i. e. the power variation across the subcarriers of the allocated uplink resource blocks. This helps to identify distortions in the frequency response, e. g. ripple effects, which may cause amplification and attenuation of certain subcarriers. Fig. 6-17 shows an example of a spectrum flatness measurement that was performed with a radio communication tester.

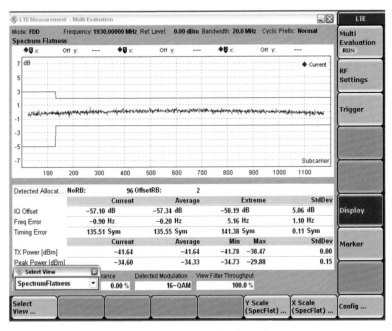

Fig. 6-17 Spectrum (channel) flatness, measured with a radio communication tester.

Another important test area for any cellular or wireless standard is the unwanted emissions in the output RF spectrum of the terminal. These can be grouped into "out-of-band emission" measurements and "spurious emissions" measurements. Out-of-band emissions occur due to imperfections in the modulation process and are identified e. g. based on the spectrum emission mask and adjacent channel leakage power ratio (ACLR). Spurious emissions measurements, on the other hand, assess harmonic emissions, parasitic emissions, intermodulation products and frequency conversion products. The out-of-band (OOB) domain is close to the transmit channel bandwidth, whereas the spurious domain lies beyond that; see Fig. 6-18.

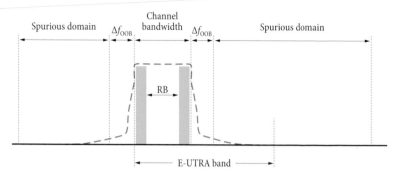

Fig. 6-18 Transmitter RF spectrum.

Source: [3GPP TS 36.521, Ref. 22], reproduced by permission of 3GPP

6.2.1.4 Output RF spectrum emissions

Occupied bandwidth (test 6.6.1)

First, the occupied bandwidth of the terminal is determined. This measurement provides the bandwidth that contains 99 % of the total integrated mean power of the transmitted spectrum. The occupied bandwidth must be less than the defined channel bandwidths 1.4 MHz, 3 MHz, 5 MHz, 10 MHz, 15 MHz, 20 MHz. The occupied bandwidth can be measured easily by performing spectrum measurements with a signal analyzer; see Fig. 6-19 for the example of an LTE FDD uplink 10 MHz signal.

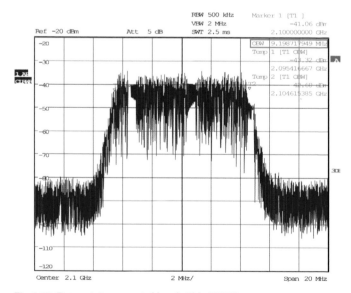

Fig. 6-19 Determining occupied bandwidth (OBW).

Spectrum emission mask (test 6.6.2.1)

The spectrum emission mask provides a detailed requirement for the spectrum of the uplink signal transmitted by the terminal. In the immediate vicinity of the occupied frequency channel, i.e. at a spacing of up to 1 MHz from the edge of the channel bandwidth (parameter Δf_{OOB} as shown in Fig. 6-18), a high-resolution measurement filter with a 30 kHz measurement bandwidth is used. At larger spacings up to 25 MHz, a wider measurement filter with 1 MHz measurement bandwidth is used. The spectrum emission mask requirements as of 3GPP TS 36.521 are shown in Fig. 6-20. A measurement example for the spectrum emission mask of an uplink 10 MHz signal is shown in Fig. 6-12.

Spectrum emission limit (dBm) / channel bandwidth							
Δf_{OOB} (MHz)	1.4 MHz	3 MHz	5 MHz	10 MHz	15 MHz	20 MHz	Measurement bandwidth
± 0 to 1	−10	−13	−15	−18	−20	−21	30 kHz
± 1 to 2.5	−10	−10	−10	−10	−10	−10	1 MHz
± 2.5 to 2.8	−25	−10	−10	−10	−10	−10	1 MHz
± 2.8 to 5		−10	−10	−10	−10	−10	1 MHz
± 5 to 6		−25	−13	−13	−13	−13	1 MHz
± 6 to 10			−25	−13	−13	−13	1 MHz
± 10 to 15				−25	−13	−13	1 MHz
± 15 to 20					−25	−13	1 MHz
± 20 to 25						−25	1 MHz

Fig. 6-20 General E-UTRA spectrum emission mask, minimum requirement.

Source: [3GPP TS 36.521, Ref. 22], reproduced by permission of 3GPP

Additional spectrum emission mask requirements (test 6.6.2.2) can be mandated by the network for specific deployment scenarios or due to regulatory reasons. The network provides an indication to the terminal if such additional (more stringent) requirements apply. The network sets the value of the information element *addionalSpectrumEmission* to NS_03, NS_04, NS_06 or NS_07 in *SystemInformationblockType2* to indicate the type of requirements. To meet these additional requirements, an additional maximum power reduction (A-MPR) may be applied for the terminal output power as stipulated in [Ref. 22].

Adjacent channel leakage power ratio (test 6.6.2.3)

Adjacent channel leakage power ratio (ACLR) is an important measure to verify that the terminal transmitter does not cause unacceptable interference to adjacent channels. [Ref. 22] differentiates whether the adjacent bands are E-UTRA or UTRA bands. Thus, ACLR is verified for different scenarios; see Fig. 6-21. Verification is performed for one adjacent E-UTRA band (E-UTRA$_{ACLR1}$) and for two UTRA bands (UTRA$_{ACLR1}$ and UTRA$_{ACLR2}$) since there is also an effect due to ACLR on the UTRA band that is not directly adjacent to the E-UTRA channel. The ACLR is then determined as the ratio of the filtered mean power on the LTE (E-UTRA) channel to the filtered mean power on an adjacent channel frequency.

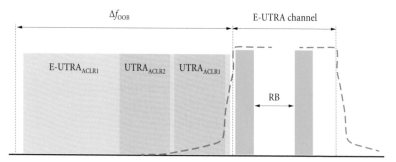

Fig. 6-21 ACLR requirements.

Source: [3GPP TS 36.521, Ref. 22], reproduced by permission of 3GPP

The minimum requirements from [Ref. 22] are shown in Fig. 6-22 for the case of an adjacent E-UTRA band and in Fig. 6-23 for the case of adjacent UTRA bands. The assigned E-UTRA channel power and adjacent E-UTRA channel power are measured with rectangular filters with measurement bandwidths specified in Fig. 6-22. The UTRA channel power is measured with a RRC bandwidth filter with roll-off factor $\alpha = 0.22$. The assigned E-UTRA channel power is measured with a rectangular filter with measurement bandwidth specified in Fig. 6-23.

Channel bandwidth / E-UTRA$_{ACLR1}$ / measurement bandwidth						
	1.4 MHz	3 MHz	5 MHz	10 MHz	15 MHz	20 MHz
E-UTRA$_{ACLR1}$	30 dB	30 dB	30 dB	30 dB	30 dB	30 dB
E-UTRA channel measurement bandwidth	1.08 MHz	2.7 MHz	4.5 MHz	9.0 MHz	13.5 MHz	18 MHz
Adjacent channel centre frequency offset (in MHz)	+1.4 / −1.4	+3 / −3	+5 / −5	+10 / −10	+15 / −15	+20 / −20

Fig. 6-22 Minimum requirements for E-UTRA$_{ACLR1}$.

Source: [3GPP TS 36.521, Ref. 22], reproduced by permission of 3GPP

Channel bandwidth / UTRA$_{ACLR1/2}$ / measurement bandwidth						
	1.4 MHz	3 MHz	5 MHz	10 MHz	15 MHz	20 MHz
UTRA$_{ACLR1}$	33 dB	33 dB	33 dB	33 dB	33 dB	33 dB
Adjacent channel center frequency offset (MHz)	$0.7 + BW_{UTRA}/2$ / $-0.7 - BW_{UTRA}/2$	$1.5 + BW_{UTRA}/2$ / $-1.5 - BW_{UTRA}/2$	$2.5 + BW_{UTRA}/2$ / $-2.5 - BW_{UTRA}/2$	$5 + BW_{UTRA}/2$ / $-5 - BW_{UTRA}/2$	$7.5 + BW_{UTRA}/2$ / $-7.5 - BW_{UTRA}/2$	$10 + BW_{UTRA}/2$ / $-10 - BW_{UTRA}/2$
UTRA$_{ACLR2}$	–	–	36 dB	36 dB	36 dB	36 dB
Adjacent channel center frequency offset (MHz)	–	–	$2.5 + 3 \cdot BW_{UTRA}/2$ / $-2.5 - 3 \cdot BW_{UTRA}/2$	$5 + 3 \cdot BW_{UTRA}/2$ / $-5 - 3 \cdot BW_{UTRA}/2$	$7.5 + 3 \cdot BW_{UTRA}/2$ / $-7.5 - 3 \cdot BW_{UTRA}/2$	$10 + 3 \cdot BW_{UTRA}/2$ / $-10 - 3 \cdot BW_{UTRA}/2$
E-UTRA channel measurement bandwidth	–	–	4.5 MHz	9 MHz	13.5 MHz	18 MHz
UTRA 5 MHz-channel measurement bandwidth[1]	–	–	3.84 MHz	3.84 MHz	3.84 MHz	3.84 MHz
UTRA 1.6 MHz-channel measurement bandwidth[2]	–	–	1.28 MHz	1.28 MHz	1.28 MHz	1.28 MHz

1) Applicable for E-UTRA FDD co-existence with UTRA FDD in paired spectrum.
2) Applicable for E-UTRA TDD co-existence with UTRA TDD in unpaired spectrum.

Fig. 6-23 Minimum requirements for UTRA$_{ACLR1/2}$.

Source: [3GPP TS 36.521, Ref. 22], reproduced by permission of 3GPP

Fig. 6-24 shows an ACLR measurement with a radio communication tester for an LTE uplink signal with 10 MHz. The blue and purple bars indicate the measured power in the operating band and in the adjacent E-UTRA and adjacent and alternate UTRA bands. The red lines reflect the ACLR limits from Fig. 6-22 and Fig. 6-23.

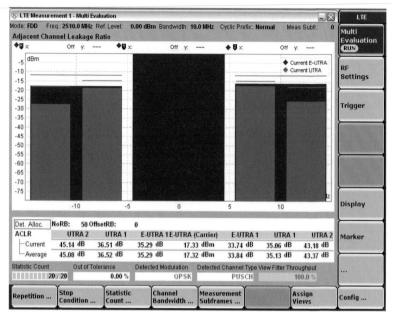

Fig. 6-24 ACLR measurement performed with a radio communication tester.

Transmitter spurious emissions (test 6.6.3.1)

Spurious emissions are caused by unwanted transmitter effects. The transmitter spurious emissions requirements apply for the frequency ranges at a distance of more than Δf_{OOB} (MHz) from the edge of the LTE channel bandwidth; see Fig. 6-18, and for an overall measurement range between 9 kHz and 12.75 GHz. Δf_{OOB} (MHz) is specified for the different LTE channel bandwidths in Fig. 6-25. The test verifies that the terminal does not cause unacceptable interference in this frequency range.

Channel bandwidth	1.4 MHz	3 MHz	5 MHz	10 MHz	15 MHz	20 MHz
Δf_{OOB} (MHz)	2.8	6	10	15	20	25

Fig. 6-25 Δf_{OOB} boundary between E-UTRA channel and spurious emission domain.

Source: [3GPP TS 36.521, Ref. 22], reproduced by permission of 3GPP

The spurious emissions limits apply for all transmitter band configurations and channel bandwidths. The minimum requirements are shown in Fig. 6-26.

Frequency range	Maximum level	Measurement bandwidth
9 kHz ≤ f < 150 kHz	–36 dBm	1 kHz
150 kHz ≤ f < 30 MHz	–36 dBm	10 kHz
30 MHz ≤ f < 1000 MHz	–36 dBm	100 kHz
1 GHz ≤ f < 12.75 GHz	–30 dBm	1 MHz

Fig. 6-26 Spurious emissions limits.

Source: [3GPP TS 36.521, Ref. 22], reproduced by permission of 3GPP

Besides these general requirements, the **spurious emission band UE coexistence requirements (test 6.6.3.2)** as stipulated in [Ref. 22] provide specific requirements to ensure protection of coexisting systems that may operate in the same or different operating bands.

Similar to the additional spectrum emission mask requirements mentioned above, the network can also mandate **additional spurious emissions (test 6.6.3.3)** requirements, which can be signaled by the network by setting the value of the information element *addionalSpectrumEmission* which is broadcast in *SystemInformationBlockType2* to NS_05, NS_07, NS_08 or NS_09.

6.2.1.5 Transmit intermodulation (test 6.7)

The transmit **intermodulation** performance is a measure of the capability of the transmitter to inhibit the generation of signals in its nonlinear elements caused by the presence of the wanted signal and an interfering signal reaching the transmitter via the antenna. Terminals transmitting in close vicinity to one other can produce intermodulation products which can fall into the terminal or base station receive band as an unwanted interfering signal. This test is based on an interfering CW signal which is added to the transmitter antenna port at a given frequency offset. The test setup is shown in Fig. 6-27. The abbreviation SS stands for system simulator and refers to the test equipment emulating the base station behavior.

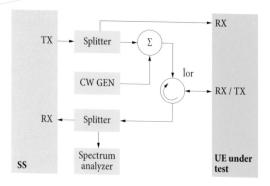

Fig. 6-27 Test setup for transmit intermodulation performance.

Source: [3GPP TS 36.508, Ref. 23], reproduced by permission of 3GPP

It should be clear from this discussion that 3GPP has defined a multitude of transmit requirements. Test equipment should ideally simplify the related work insofar as possible.

Fig. 6-28 shows a screenshot from a radio communication tester with RF measurement results from a terminal's uplink transmission. Several measurements are represented in multi-evaluation mode, i.e. from one and the same received signal section, different measurements are evaluated. Fig. 6-28 shows the results for EVM, inband emissions, spectrum flatness, spectrum emission mask, ACLR, TX power, IQ offset, frequency error and much more.

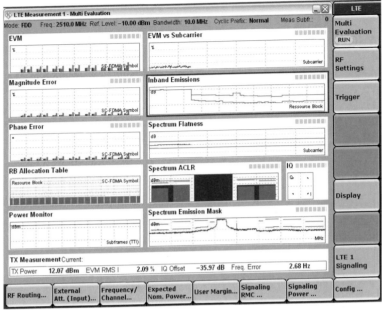

Fig. 6-28 Terminal RF measurements performed with a radio communication tester in multi-evaluation mode.

6.2.2 Receiver characteristics

Fig. 6-29 gives an overview of the receiver tests specified in 3GPP TS 36.521 [Ref. 22].

I **Reference sensitivity level**
I **Maximum input level**
I **Adjacent channel selectivity (ACS)**
I **Blocking characteristics:** In-band blocking, out-of-band blocking, narrowband blocking
I **Spurious response**
I **Intermodulation characteristics:** Wideband intermodulation
I **Spurious emissions**

Fig. 6-29 LTE terminal receiver tests.

Receiver characteristics are verified based on the downlink reference measurement channels specified in [Ref. 22], i.e. so-called fixed reference channels. Fig. 6-30 shows an example of the downlink fixed reference channel for receiver requirements for FDD, and Fig. 6-31 for TDD (applicable in the above-mentioned receiver tests except the maximum input level test). One configuration is provided for each bandwidth. By way of example, the parameterization for the 10 MHz bandwidth is highlighted. The detailed configuration of the fixed reference channels is important in order to have a well-defined reference for testing. Besides the exact allocation and modulation parameters, the coding and HARQ parameters are specified. The maximum achievable throughput for each fixed reference channel is also listed: It is the reference for the test criterion used for all receiver tests except for spurious emissions as described hereafter.

Parameter	Unit	Value					
Channel bandwidth	MHz	1.4	3	5	10	15	20
Allocated resource blocks		6	15	25	50	75	100
Subcarriers per resource block		12	12	12	12	12	12
Allocated subframes per radio frame		10	10	10	10	10	10
Modulation		QPSK	QPSK	QPSK	QPSK	QPSK	QPSK
Target coding rate		1/3	1/3	1/3	1/3	1/3	1/3
Number of HARQ processes		8	8	8	8	8	8
Maximum number of HARQ transmissions		1	1	1	1	1	1
Information bit payload per subframe							
For subframes 1, 2, 3, 4, 6, 7, 8, 9	bit	408	1320	2216	4392	6712	8760
For subframe 5	bit	n/a	n/a	n/a	n/a	n/a	n/a
For subframe 0	bit	152	872	1800	4392	6712	8760
Transport block CRC	bit	24	24	24	24	24	24
Number of code blocks per subframe							
For subframes 1, 2, 3, 4, 6, 7, 8, 9	bit	1	1	1	1	2	2
For subframe 5	bit	n/a	n/a	n/a	n/a	n/a	n/a
For subframe 0	bit	1	1	1	1	2	2
Binary channel bits per subframe							
For subframes 1, 2, 3, 4, 6, 7, 8, 9	bit	1368	3780	6300	13800	20700	27600
For subframe 5	bit	n/a	n/a	n/a	n/a	n/a	n/a
For subframe 0	bit	528	2940	5460	12960	19860	26760
Max. throughput averaged over 1 frame	kbps	341.6	1143.2	1952.8	3952.8	6040.8	7884
UE category		1 to 5	1 to 5	1 to 5	1 to 5	1 to 5	1 to 5

Fig. 6-30 Fixed reference channel for receiver requirements for FDD.

Source: [3GPP TS 36.521, Ref. 22], reproduced by permission of 3GPP

Parameter	Unit	Value					
Channel bandwidth	MHz	1.4	3	5	10	15	20
Allocated resource blocks		6	15	25	50	75	100
Uplink-downlink configuration		1	1	1	1	1	1
Allocated subframes per radio frame (D + S)		4	4 + 2	4 + 2	4 + 2	4 + 2	4 + 2
Number of HARQ processes		7	7	7	7	7	7
Maximum number of HARQ transmission		1	1	1	1	1	1
Modulation		QPSK	QPSK	QPSK	QPSK	QPSK	QPSK
Target coding rate		1/3	1/3	1/3	1/3	1/3	1/3
Information bit payload per subframe	bit						
For subframe 4, 9		408	1320	2216	4392	6712	8760
For subframe 1, 6		n/a	968	1544	3240	4968	6712
For subframe 5		n/a	n/a	n/a	n/a	n/a	n/a
For subframe 0		208	1064	1800	4392	6712	8760
Transport block CRC	bit	24	24	24	24	24	24
Number of code blocks per subframe							
For subframe 4, 9		1	1	1	1	2	2
For subframe 1, 6		n/a	1	1	1	1	2
For subframe 5		n/a	n/a	n/a	n/a	n/a	n/a
For subframe 0		1	1	1	1	2	2
Binary channel bits per subframe	bit						
For subframe 4, 9		1368	3780	6300	13800	20700	27600
For subframe 1, 6		n/a	3276	5556	11256	16956	22656
For subframe 5		n/a	n/a	n/a	n/a	n/a	n/a
For subframe 0		672	3084	5604	13104	20004	26904
Max. throughput averaged over 1 frame	kbps	102.4	564	932	1965.6	3007.2	3970.4
UE category		1 to 5	1 to 5	1 to 5	1 to 5	1 to 5	1 to 5

Fig. 6-31 Fixed reference channel for receiver requirements for TDD.

Source: [3GPP TS 36.521, Ref. 22], reproduced by permission of 3GPP

All of the tests described hereafter (except for spurious emissions) use the achievable throughput as a criterion. An example of a throughput measurement performed with a radio communication tester is shown in Fig. 6-32. The throughput is evaluated in the tester based on the ACK / NACKs received from the terminal for the transmitted downlink packets. Most of the receiver tests require a complex test setup consisting of several test instruments, e.g. a combination of a radio communication tester and a signal generator for modeling interferers, or even a complete test system to perform full RF conformance tests.

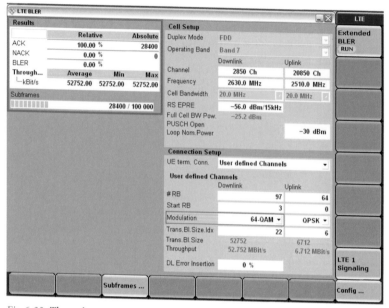

Fig. 6-32 Throughput measurement performed with a radiocommunication tester.

6.2.2.1 Reference sensitivity level (test 7.3)

The test on reference sensitivity level verifies the sensitivity of the terminal's receiver. A downlink fixed reference channel with a very low power level $P_{REFSENS}$ (e.g. $P_{REFSENS} = -97$ dBm as the minimum requirement for the 10 MHz case and E-UTRA band 1) is used as the test signal. The test then verifies the ability of the terminal to receive data on this reference channel with a given average throughput. The terminal shall achieve a throughput ≥ 95 % of the maximum throughput for the tested reference measurement channel. The test of receiver sensitivity is crucial for ensuring sufficient coverage for a base station. A terminal unable to meet the throughput requirement under the given conditions will decrease the effective coverage area of a base station.

6.2.2.2 Maximum input level (test 7.4)

Maximum input level tests the terminal receiver's ability to operate in conditions with high signal level. The wanted signal mean power is –25 dBm. This test is important because a terminal unable to meet the throughput requirement under these conditions will decrease the coverage area in the vicinity of a base station.

6.2.2.3 Adjacent channel selectivity – ACS (test 7.5)

Adjacent channel selectivity tests the terminal's ability to achieve a throughput target in the presence of an adjacent channel signal at a given frequency offset from the center frequency of the assigned channel. The adjacent channel signal emulates the signal from another nearby base station. The test is performed with two different power settings for the wanted signal and interfering signal in accordance with the test setup shown in Fig. 6-33.

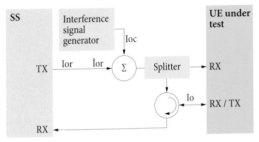

Fig. 6-33 Test setup for adjacent channel selectivity.

Source: [3GPP TS 36.508, Ref. 23], reproduced by permission of 3GPP

6.2.2.4 Blocking characteristics

The blocking characteristics are a measure of the receiver's ability to receive a wanted signal at its assigned channel frequency in the presence of an unwanted interferer with specific characteristics. Depending on the frequency offset of the interferer with respect to the assigned channel frequency, [Ref. 22] differentiates between the following:

In-band blocking (test 7.6.1)
The interfering E-UTRA signal lies in the range from 15 MHz below to 15 MHz above the terminal receive band.

Out-of-band blocking (test 7.6.2)
The interfering signal lies more than 15 MHz below or above the terminal's receive band. In contrast to in-band blocking, a CW signal is used for testing out-of-band blocking. Different frequency offsets for the interferer with a step size of 1 MHz are tested. The frequencies where the throughput requirement is not met are recorded and reverified later in the spurious response test.

Narrow-band blocking (test 7.6.3)

This is defined for an interfering CW signal at a frequency close to the terminal's receive band (offset is less than the nominal channel spacing).

6.2.2.5 Spurious response (test 7.7)

Interferers on adjacent channels or on frequencies where a spurious response occurs are not evaluated as part of the blocking tests since these frequencies are covered by separate requirements. The test on spurious response is also based on a CW interfering signal. The interferer is set at specific frequencies where a spurious response is obtained, i.e. where the out-of-band blocking requirements were not met.

6.2.2.6 Intermodulation characteristics

Wideband intermodulation (test 7.8.1)

The test on wideband intermodulation requires both a CW interferer and a modulated E-UTRA interferer which have a specific frequency relationship with respect to the wanted signal. The interfering signals produce intermodulation products falling into the terminal's receive range and the test measures the receiver's capability for intermodulation response rejection.

6.2.2.7 Spurious emissions (test 7.9)

The spurious emissions power is the power of emissions generated or amplified in a receiver that appear at the terminal's antenna connector. Excess spurious emissions increase the interference to other systems. The test can be performed with a spectrum analyzer by sweeping over the frequency range of interest and measuring the spurious emissions at the receiver antenna ports.

6.2.3 Performance requirements

Performance requirements address the overall operation of the LTE physical layer, including data reception, control channel performance and correct working of control procedures.

Reporting of channel state information verifies the correct operation of the terminal's channel quality indicator (CQI) reporting as well as the terminal's precoding matrix indicator (PMI) and rank indicator (RI) reporting. This is crucial since the reported channel state information is used by the base station to make scheduling decisions and adapt the data rate to the terminal accordingly. This procedure therefore determines the overall system performance.

Performance tests are captured in dedicated sections in [Ref. 22]. Fig. 6-34 shows an overview of the performance tests. In the specification, these tests contain a multitude of different subtests to cover a wide selection of configuration options. This chapter attempts to provide a rough overview.

- **Demodulation of PDSCH (cell-specific reference symbols) for FDD and TDD:** Single antenna port performance, transmit diversity performance, open loop spatial multiplexing performance, closed loop spatial multiplexing performance
- **Demodulation of PDSCH for TDD (user-specific reference symbols)**
- **Demodulation of PCFICH/PDCCH for FDD and TDD:** Single antenna port performance and transmit diversity performance
- **Demodulation of PHICH for FDD and TDD:** Single antenna port performance and transmit diversity performance
- **Reporting of channel quality indicator (CQI) for FDD and TDD:** CQI reporting under AWGN and fading conditions
- **Reporting of precoding matrix indicator (PMI) for FDD and TDD:** Single PMI and multiple PMI
- **Reporting of rank indicator (RI) for FDD and TDD**

Fig. 6-34 LTE terminal performance tests.

Similarly to the receiver tests, performance tests are also based on fixed reference channels that are specific to the given test purpose. Due to the high number of performance tests, there is also a high number of fixed reference channels defined with different MIMO configurations or a different control channel setup. An example of a fixed reference channel is shown in Fig. 6-35. This is a TDD fixed reference channel to verify multi-antenna transmission with two antenna ports and a single transmission layer.

Reference channel	R.10 TDD
Channel bandwidth	10 MHz
Allocated resource blocks	50
Uplink-downlink configuration	1
Allocated subframes per radio frame (D + S)	4 + 2
Modulation	QPSK
Target coding rate	1/3
Information bit payload	
For subframes 4, 9	4392 bit
For subframes 1, 6	3240 bit
For subframe 5	n/a
For subframe 0	4392 bit
Number of code blocks per subframe	
For subframes 4, 9	1
For subframes 1, 6	1
For subframe 5	n/a
For subframe 0	1
Binary channel bits per subframe	
For subframes 4, 9	13 200 bit
For subframes 1, 6	10 656 bit
For subframe 5	n/a
For subframe 0	12 528 bit
Max. throughput averaged over 1 frame	1.966 Mbps
UE category	1 to 5

Fig. 6-35 TDD R.10 fixed reference channel.

Source: [3GPP TS 36.521, Ref. 22], reproduced by permission of 3GPP

In order to take into account realistic propagation conditions, simulation of fading and AWGN is mandated for performance tests. Furthermore, an **OFDMA channel noise generator (OCNG)** is used for performance tests to model the traffic in unused physical resource blocks. OCNG simulates the presence of other terminals. These "virtual UEs" are simulated with uncorrelated pseudorandom data (QPSK modulated). Different OCNG patterns (OP) exist for FDD and TDD and for different bandwidths.

6.2.3.1 Demodulation of PDSCH (cell-specific reference symbols, specification chapter 8.2)

The focus of the performance tests for PDSCH data demodulation is to verify the terminal's ability to receive a predefined test signal with a target throughput under clearly defined conditions. This includes the definition of the propagation conditions, antenna configuration and MIMO channel correlation matrix (see 6.4, page 161) as well as the signal-to-noise ratio. Regular HARQ operation is assumed during the test.

For verifying full conformance to the standard, signaling functionality is required for the performance tests (as well as for the terminal transmitter and receiver tests). The system simulator places the terminal in a well-defined test mode by activating the "UE test mode procedure" [Ref. 27]. No real application data is sent via the downlink reference measurement channel. Instead, the system simulator sends MAC padding bits.

The test setup for the 1×2 antenna configuration (1 transmit antenna, 2 receive antennas) is shown in Fig. 6-36.

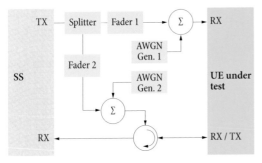

Fig. 6-36 Test setup for PDSCH performance requirements with antenna configuration 1×2.

Source: [3GPP TS 36.508, Ref. 23], reproduced by permission of 3GPP

In Fig. 6-37, the 18 different subtests for this antenna configuration and for the FDD case are listed. The test conditions and parameters as well as the minimum performance requirements in terms of a throughput target are described. The reference channels used for the tests represent different modulation and coding schemes and different bandwidth allocations. For a description of the propagation conditions extended vehicular A (EVA) and extended typical urban (ETU) and the correlation matrix, please refer to chapter 6.4, page 161. The abbreviation HST refers to propagation conditions in the high speed train scenario. Not all tests are relevant for all UE categories (see chapter 5.8, page 94 for the definition of the UE categories). Therefore, applicability to UE categories is listed as well. The table illustrates the large amount of test cases for this antenna configuration alone.

Test number	Band-width (MHz)	Refer-ence channel	OCNG pattern	Propa-gation condi-tion	Correlation matrix and antenna configuration	Reference value		UE category
						Fraction of maximum throughput (%)	SNR (dB)	
1	10	R.2 FDD	OP.1 FDD	EVA5	1×2 low	70	−1.0	1 to 5
2	10	R.2 FDD	OP.1 FDD	ETU70	1×2 low	70	−0.4	1 to 5
3	10	R.2 FDD	OP.1 FDD	ETU300	1×2 low	70	0.0	1 to 5
4	10	R.2 FDD	OP.1 FDD	HST	1×2 low	70	−2.4	1 to 5
5	1.4	R.4 FDD	OP.1 FDD	EVA5	1×2 low	70	−0.5	1 to 5
6	10	R.3 FDD	OP.1 FDD	EVA5	1×2 low	70	6.7	2 to 5
7	10	R.3 FDD	OP.1 FDD	ETU70	1×2 low	30	1.4	2 to 5
8	10	R.3 FDD	OP.1 FDD	ETU300	1×2 high	70	9.4	2 to 5
9	3	R.5 FDD	OP.1 FDD	EVA5	1×2 low	70	17.6	1 to 5
10	5	R.6 FDD	OP.1 FDD	EVA5	1×2 low	70	17.4	2 to 5
11	10	R.7 FDD	OP.1 FDD	EVA5	1×2 low	70	17.7	2 to 5
12	10	R.7 FDD	OP.1 FDD	ETU70	1×2 low	70	19.0	2 to 5
13	10	R.7 FDD	OP.1 FDD	EVA5	1×2 high	70	19.1	2 to 5
14	15	R.8 FDD	OP.1 FDD	EVA5	1×2 low	70	17.7	2 to 5
15	20	R.9 FDD	OP.1 FDD	EVA5	1×2 low	70	17.6	3 to 5
16	3	R.0 FDD	OP.1 FDD	ETU70	1×2 low	30	1.9	1 to 5
17	10	R.1 FDD	OP.1 FDD	ETU70	1×2 low	30	1.9	1 to 5
18	20	R.1 FDD	OP.1 FDD	ETU70	1×2 low	30	1.9	1 to 5

Fig. 6-37 Minimum performance requirements for PDSCH demodulation (1×2 antenna configuration).

Source: [3GPP TS 36.521, Ref. 22], reproduced by permission of 3GPP

The PDSCH demodulation test for verifying transmit diversity and spatial multiplexing performance requires a more complex test setup to take into account 2×2 and 4×2 antenna configurations. Fig. 6-38 shows the test setup used for testing transmit diversity performance, open loop spatial multiplexing performance and closed loop spatial multiplexing performance with a 2×2 antenna configuration. Four fading channels are simulated to model the channels between each transmit and receive antenna. AWGN is also applied. The 4×2 antenna configuration represents an even more extended setup, requiring eight fading channel simulations.

In terms of closed loop spatial multiplexing, both single-layer and multi-layer performance scenarios are tested. MIMO reporting is configured as well.

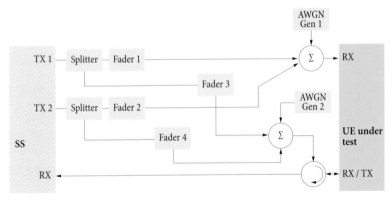

Fig. 6-38 Test setup for PDSCH performance test with antenna configuration 2×2.

Source: [3GPP TS 36.508, Ref. 23], reproduced by permission of 3GPP

6.2.3.2 Demodulation of PDSCH (user-specific reference symbols, specification chapter 8.3)

The test on PDSCH demodulation with user-specific reference symbols is defined for TDD. User-specific reference symbols are used in beamforming scenarios. The test is specified for a 10 MHz bandwidth scenario. Four subtests are defined, addressing each of the modulation schemes QPSK, 16QAM and 64QAM with full (50) resource block allocation and additionally a test with 16QAM modulation and a single allocated resource block. The control channels PBCH, PDCCH and PCFICH and the cell-specific reference symbols are transmitted on one antenna port (test setup as in Fig. 6-38). The PDSCH with the associated dedicated reference symbols is transmitted on both antennas via beamforming, corresponding to virtual antenna port 5. The beam-forming channel is modeled as follows: Random single-layer 2×1 pre-coders from the LTE MIMO codebook (Fig. 5-37) are applied such that an effective channel matrix H_{eff} results [Ref. 22], which ensues from the channel matrix in accordance with the propagation conditions and the applied precoders.

6.2.3.3 Demodulation of PCFICH / PDCCH (specification chapter 8.4)

The PCFICH / PDCCH demodulation performance is verified for a single-antenna port as well as for transmit diversity scenarios with two and four transmit antennas, both for FDD and TDD. The test set-ups for single antenna port performance and 2×2 transmit diversity performance are the same as shown in Fig. 6-36 and Fig. 6-38, respec-tively. The receiver characteristics of the PDCCH / PCFICH are deter-mined by the probability of missed detection of the downlink sched-uling grant sent on the PDCCH. The PDCCH and PCFICH are tested jointly, i.e. missed detection of the PCFICH implies a missed detec-tion of the PDCCH. Configuration of the PDCCH is defined by refer-ence measurement channels. Two OFDM symbols are allocated for the PDCCH. The missed detection is verified as follows: The system simu-lator continues to schedule downlink data (actually MAC padding bits on a specified downlink reference measurement channel) to the termi-nal and evaluates the uplink ACK / NACK feedback on the PUCCH. Whenever ACK or NACK is received, it can be assumed that the termi-nal detected the PCFICH / PDCCH and demodulated the associated PDSCH. In case the terminal does not respond on the PUCCH with an ACK or NACK where it should (this event is referred to as "statDTX" in the test specification [Ref. 22]), a missed detection of PCFICH / PDCCH can be assumed.

6.2.3.4 Demodulation of PHICH (specification chapter 8.5)

The PHICH demodulation performance is based on the average prob-ability of missed detection of the hybrid ARQ indicator ("ACK to NACK") for the specified reference measurement channels. As before, the single-antenna port performance and 2×2 and 4×2 transmit diver-sity performance are evaluated for FDD and TDD, with the test set-ups described above for the corresponding PCFICH / PDCCH demod-ulation tests. The system simulator schedules PUSCH transmissions in eight consecutive transmission time intervals to the terminal. Accordingly, the terminal responds by transmitting on the PUSCH. MAC padding bits are sent as the data payload (since no application data is available). The system simulator acknowledges these uplink transmissions on the PHICH resource assigned to these users. Note that the reference measurement channels defined for this test also include modeling of up to two interfering users on the PHICH. The terminal is then expected to not respond with any PUSCH retransmissions. If these retransmissions occur, the system simulator assumes that the ACK on the PHICH beforehand was not detected correctly. The test is repeated until statistical significance is achieved and the probability of missed detection of the hybrid ARQ indicator is determined.

The test pattern for the PHICH test for FDD is shown in Fig. 6-39.

TTI	1 to 4	5 to 8	9 to 12	13 to 16	17 to 20	21 to 24
PDCCH	S	S	–	–	S	S
PHICH	–	–	A	A	–	–
PUSCH	–	T	T	R	R	T
UL HARQ Process	1 to 4	5 to 8	1 to 4	5 to 8	1 to 4	5 to 8

Note 1: This table gives an example test pattern for the HARQ process for the FDD PHICH test.
Note 2: The following notation is used:
    S: Represents sending PDCCH DCI format 0 to schedule a future PUSCH transmission.
    A: Represents the ACK transmission on the PHICH.
    T: Represents a scheduled PUSCH transmission.
    R: Represents a potential PUSCH re-transmission due to a missed ACK.

Fig. 6-39 PHICH test pattern (FDD).
Source: [3GPP TS 36.521, Ref. 22], reproduced by permission of 3GPP

6.2.3.5 CQI reporting
For verifying CQI reporting, a similar test procedure to the one known from HSDPA is used. However, due to an increase in the configuration options, the test has been extended for LTE. The test is performed for both AWGN and fading conditions and for different PUCCH or PUSCH reporting modes.

CQI reporting under AWGN conditions – PUCCH 1-0
(specification chapter 9.2.1)
In the case of **CQI reporting under AWGN conditions**, the CQI reporting performance is verified based on two criteria corresponding to two test steps: The reporting variance determines whether the terminal is able to report consistent CQI values on the PUCCH for well-

defined fixed channel conditions (SNR and reference measurement channel): The reported CQI value shall be in the range of ±1 of the reported median greater than 90 % of the time. The median CQI value is the value that divides the group of reported CQI values such that half of the reported CQI values are lower than the median and the other half are higher than the median. The system simulator in this test does not respond to the CQI reports from the terminal in order to maintain fixed conditions.

In a second test step, it is verified that the reported CQI values conform to the expected block error rate (BLER) performance, i. e. the transport format indicated by the median CQI corresponds to a 10 % block error rate on the PDSCH. For this purpose, the system simulator schedules PDSCH transmissions with the transport format corresponding to the median CQI that was determined in the first test step and evaluates the ACK / NACK responses on the PUCCH. This is also repeated for PDSCH transmissions with transport formats in accordance with the median CQI + 1 and median CQI −1. As a result, the 10 % BLER threshold must be reflected; otherwise, the terminal is deemed to fail the test.

CQI reporting under AWGN conditions – PUCCH 1-1 (specification chapter 9.2.2)

In the case of MIMO spatial multiplexing, the terminal can evaluate CQI values for two code words. It signals a wideband CQI for the first code word as well as an offset value for the second code word. The test principle described above for the single code word case under AWGN conditions is then applied accordingly to this reporting mode.

CQI reporting under fading conditions – frequency-selective scheduling mode (specification chapter 9.3.1)

CQI reporting under fading conditions is also investigated. A special propagation channel is modeled to investigate **frequency-selective channel conditions.** In this situation, it is of interest to verify the performance of the subband CQI reporting. The system simulator transmits the PDSCH with a fixed transport format and collects both wideband and subband CQI reports. The median for the wideband CQI values is then evaluated and the throughput t_{median} for the PDSCH based on the transport format associated with the median wideband CQI value is determined in a randomly selected subband. In a second step, the throughput $t_{subband}$ is measured based on the subbands where the highest subband CQI value was reported in each subframe and the PDSCH is formatted in accordance with this value. The throughput ratio $t_{subband}/t_{median}$ is then determined to evaluate the performance increase for frequency-selective subband based scheduling.

CQI reporting under fading conditions – frequency non-selective scheduling mode (specification chapter 9.3.2)

The test on CQI reporting in frequency non-selective scheduling mode verifies that the terminal tracks channel variations correctly and always selects the largest possible transport format. The system simulator adapts the PDSCH transport format to the wideband CQI values proposed by the terminal. The resulting throughput $t_{wideband}$ and the ratio $t_{wideband}/t_{median}$ are determined, and this ratio must be higher than the specified performance threshold. The throughput t_{median} is derived by the system simulator by scheduling PDSCH with the transport format in accordance with the wideband median CQI value determined in a first test step with fixed test conditions (regardless of the UE CQI report).

CQI reporting under fading conditions – frequency-selective interference (specification chapter 9.3.3)

The performance of subband CQI reporting is verified furthermore in a test based on frequency-selective interference. For a 10 MHz scenario, interference is modeled such that one subband at the channel edge should be preferred by the terminal. The test determines whether the terminal identifies this subband and reports the higher subband CQI value. In another test step, the throughput $t_{subband}$ is evaluated for scheduling in this subband with the transport format in accordance with the reported subband CQI value. $t_{subband}/t_{median}$ must be above the defined threshold, where t_{median} is based on the transport format associated with the median wideband CQI value scheduled in a randomly selected subband.

6.2.3.6 Reporting of precoding matrix indicator (PMI, specification chapter 9.4)

Reporting of the precoding matrix indicator (PMI) verifies the performance of the terminal's PMI reports. The base station uses the reported PMI to adapt the MIMO precoding so this procedure has an immediate impact on the data rate and throughput performance. The test criterion is the precoding gain, which is the relative increase in throughput when the base station transmitter is configured in accordance with the terminal's PMI reports, compared to the case in which the base station transmitter uses random precoding. PDSCH transmission mode 6 is assumed (see chapter 5.5.2, page 54). The test is performed for reporting of a single PMI as well as for reporting of multiple PMIs for the different subbands.

6.2.3.7 Reporting of rank indicator (RI, specification chapter 9.5)

Reporting of the rank indicator (RI) verifies that the reported rank indicator accurately represents the channel rank. Transmission mode 4 (see chapter 5.5.2, page 54) is used for the test. The performance increase when adapting to the rank proposed by the terminal is measured and compared to the use of a fixed rank for PDSCH transmission. The test is performed for a fixed rank of 1 and 2. The resulting throughput t_{fix} is compared to the throughput $t_{reported}$ for adaptive rank transmission. The transport format selection in the system simulator is carried out based on wideband CQI feedback.

6.3 Base station RF testing

3GPP Technical Specification 36.141 [Ref. 24] specifies RF conformance tests that LTE FDD and TDD base stations must comply with. The specification is based on the RF requirements for LTE base stations captured in 3GPP TS 36.104 [Ref. 25] which provides the minimum requirements. The test requirements in 3GPP TS 36.141 [Ref. 24] have been calculated by typically relaxing the minimum requirements from 3GPP TS 36.104 [Ref. 25], i.e. applying an additional test tolerance in order to take into account test procedure uncertainties.

The following chapters provide an overview of the RF conformance tests for LTE base stations as specified in 3GPP TS 36.141 [Ref. 24], including transmitter, receiver and performance tests. Whenever useful, the chapter of the relevant specification [Ref. 24] to which a certain paragraph refers is indicated. Note that the tests are not necessarily discussed in the same order found in the specification.

The tests must be performed as a function of the operating bands, frequency ranges within these operating bands and channel bandwidths supported by the base station. Typically, the tests do not have to be performed for all of the supported frequencies, but rather at just three frequencies in the bottom (B), middle (M) and top (T) channels of the supported frequency range of the base station. [Ref. 24] indicates two categories of limits to be fulfilled by the base station for the measurement class of unwanted emissions: Category A applies in general and specifies relaxed limits compared to Category B, which applies only to Europe.

As before, 3GPP TS 36.141 [Ref. 24] refers to conformance testing that is relevant to manufacturers of base stations so they can declare to their customers that their products conform to the 3GPP standard. In practice, as was mentioned previously, 3GPP TS 36.141 [Ref. 24] is used as a guideline for deriving test plans beginning during early R&D for base stations. On the other hand, manufacturers can perform additional testing that goes beyond the 3GPP requirements in order to test particular features more thoroughly and fulfill additional quality and customer requirements.

6.3.1 Transmitter characteristics

Fig. 6-40 provides an overview of the transmitter tests specified in [Ref. 24].

I **Base station output power**
I **Output power dynamics:** Resource element (RE) power control dynamic range, total power dynamic range
I **Transmit ON/OFF power:** Transmitter OFF power, transmitter transient period
I **Transmitted signal quality:** Frequency error, error vector magnitude (EVM), time alignment between transmitter branches, downlink reference signal power
I **Unwanted emissions:** Occupied bandwidth, adjacent channel leakage power ratio (ACLR), operating band unwanted emissions, transmitter spurious emissions
I **Transmitter intermodulation**

Fig. 6-40 LTE base station transmitter tests.

E-UTRA test models (E-TM) describing the downlink physical channel configuration and power settings are defined for performing transmitter tests under clearly defined reference conditions. The data content of the different channels is also specified. The test models are defined for a single antenna port, 10 ms duration and one code word (transport block) without precoding. For TDD, uplink-downlink configuration 3 and special subframe configuration 8 are used. As an example, E-TM1.1 is shown in Fig. 6-41. It is valid for FDD and TDD and used e. g. for base station output power and unwanted emissions tests.

Parameter	1.4 MHz	3 MHz	5 MHz	10 MHz	15 MHz	20 MHz
Reference, synchronization signals						
RS boosting, $P_B = E_B/E_A$	1	1	1	1	1	1
Synchronization signal EPRE/E_{RS} [dB]	0.000	0.000	0.000	0.000	0.000	0.000
Reserved EPRE / E_{RS} [dB]	-inf	-inf	-inf	-inf	-inf	-inf
PBCH						
PBCH EPRE / E_{RS} [dB]	0.000	0.000	0.000	0.000	0.000	0.000
Reserved EPRE / E_{RS} [dB]	-inf	-inf	-inf	-inf	-inf	-inf
PCFICH						
# of symbols used for control channels	2	1	1	1	1	1
PCFICH EPRE / E_{RS} [dB]	3.222	0	0	0	0	0
PHICH						
# of PHICH groups	1	1	1	2	2	3
# of PHICH per group	2	2	2	2	2	2
PHICH BPSK symbol power / E_{RS} [dB]	−3.010	−3.010	−3.010	−3.010	−3.010	−3.010
PHICH group EPRE / E_{RS} [dB]	0	0	0	0	0	0
PDCCH						
# of available REGs	23	23	43	90	140	187
# of PDCCH	2	2	2	5	7	10
# of CCEs per PDCCH	1	1	2	2	2	2
# of REGs per CCE	9	9	9	9	9	9
# of REGs allocated to PDCCH	18	18	36	90	126	180
# of <NIL> REGs added for padding	5	5	7	0	14	7
PDCCH REG EPRE / E_{RS} [dB]	0.792	2.290	1.880	1.065	1.488	1.195
<NIL> REG EPRE / E_{RS} [dB]	-inf	-inf	-inf	-inf	-inf	-inf
PDSCH						
# of QPSK PDSCH PRBs which are boosted	6	15	25	50	75	100
PRB $P_A = E_A/E_{RS}$ [dB]	0	0	0	0	0	0
# of QPSK PDSCH PRBs which are de-boosted	0	0	0	0	0	0
PRB $P_A = E_A/E_{RS}$ [dB]	n.a.	n.a.	n.a.	n.a.	n.a.	n.a.

Fig. 6-41 Physical channel parameters of E-TM1.1.

Source: [3GPP TS 36.141, Ref. 24], reproduced by permission of 3GPP

EPRE means "energy per resource element". The term E_A refers to the EPRE of PDSCH resource elements in OFDM symbols that do not include reference symbols. The term E_B indicates the same, but for PDSCH resource elements in OFDM symbols that do include reference symbols. E_{RS} indicates the EPRE of reference symbol resource elements. By using these definitions, the power setting of the physical channels can be exactly defined.

Of course, the test equipment used for base station testing must support all of the test models. Fig. 6-42 shows the menu of a signal generator in which the E-TMs can be selected so the signal generator is configured to transmit such a signal. The signal can then be used e.g. for testing amplifiers or other components of the base station transmitter.

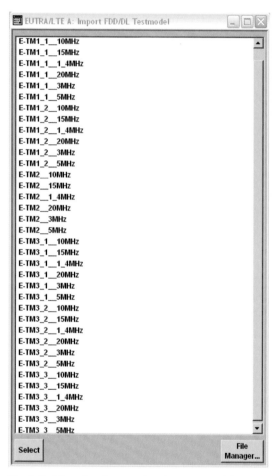

Fig. 6-42 Menu for selection of E-UTRA test model (E-TM) in a signal generator.

6.3.1.1 Base station output power (test 6.2)

Now let us have a closer look at the different transmitter tests, starting with base station output power. The test purpose is to verify the accuracy of the maximum output power across the frequency range under normal and extreme conditions for all transmitters in the base station. Extreme conditions are defined as special states in terms of the temperature, vibration, power supply, etc. There is no fixed limit for the base station maximum output power, but there is a requirement that the maximum output power must remain within a defined tolerance (minimum requirement is ±2 dB under normal conditions) with respect to the manufacturer's rated output power.

6.3.1.2 Output power dynamics
RE power control dynamic range (test 6.3.1)

The resource element (RE) power control dynamic range is the difference between the power of an RE and the average RE power for a base station at maximum output power. Fig. 6-43 shows the requirement as stated in [36.104, Ref. 25], but there is no specific conformance test described in [36.141, Ref. 24]. The EVM test instead provides sufficient test coverage for this requirement.

Modulation scheme used on the RE	RE power control dynamic range (dB)	
	(down)	(up)
QPSK (PDCCH)	–6	+4
QPSK (PDSCH)	–6	+3
16QAM (PDSCH)	–3	+3
64QAM (PDSCH)	0	0
NOTE: Total TX power shall always be less or equal to maximum BS output power.		

Fig. 6-43 E-UTRA BS RE power control dynamic range.

Source: [3GPP TS 36.104, Ref. 25], reproduced by permission of 3GPP

Total power dynamic range (test 6.3.2)

The total power dynamic range is the difference between the maximum and minimum transmit power of an OFDM symbol. The upper limit is the OFDM symbol power for a base station at maximum output power. The lower limit of the dynamic range is the OFDM symbol power for a base station when one resource block is transmitted. For measuring total power dynamic range, the OFDM symbol power is first measured based on E-TM3.1 (maximum power with all 64QAM resource blocks allocated) and then based on E-TM2 (single 64QAM resource block allocation). The difference between these two measurements is then taken. The minimum requirement for this test is shown in Fig. 6-44.

E-UTRA channel bandwidth (MHz)	Total power dynamic range (dB)
1.4	7.7
3	11.7
5	13.9
10	16.9
15	18.7
20	20

Fig. 6-44 E-UTRA BS total power dynamic range, minimum requirement.

Source: [3GPP TS 36.104, Ref. 25], reproduced by permission of 3GPP

6.3.1.3 Transmit ON/OFF power

Transmitter OFF power (test 6.4.1) /

Transmitter transient period (test 6.4.2)

Special transmitter tests apply for TDD base stations in order to verify the transmit ON/OFF power switching characteristics of the TDD signal. These tests are known as transmitter OFF power and transmitter transient period. Transmitter OFF power verifies that the transmitter OFF power spectral density is less than –85 dBm/MHz (minimum requirement). The transmitter transient period for TDD base stations is the time period during which the transmitter switches from the OFF period to the ON period or vice versa; see Fig. 6-45.

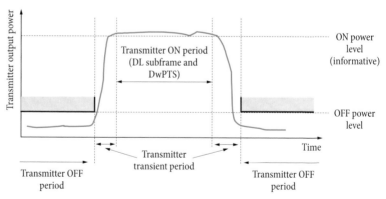

Fig. 6-45 Transmitter ON period, transmitter OFF period and transmitter transient period.

Source: [3GPP TS 36.141, Ref. 24], reproduced by permission of 3GPP

The requirements are shown in Fig. 6-46.

Transition	Transient period length [µs]
OFF to ON	17
ON to OFF	17

Fig. 6-46 Minimum requirements for the transmitter transient period.

Source: [3GPP TS 36.104, Ref. 25], reproduced by permission of 3GPP

The following tests again apply for both FDD and TDD base stations.

6.3.1.4 Transmitted signal quality

Frequency error (test 6.5.1)

The frequency error is a measure of the difference between the actual base station transmit frequency and the assigned frequency. In accordance with [Ref. 25], the base station shall be accurate to within ±0.05 ppm (minimum requirement) observed over a period of one subframe.

Error vector magnitude (test 6.5.2)

The error vector magnitude (EVM) is an established criterion for determining transmit signal quality. It is a measure of the difference between the ideal symbols and the measured symbols after equalization. This difference is called the error vector. The EVM result is defined as the square root of the ratio of the mean error vector power to the mean reference power expressed as a percentage. Fig. 6-47 shows the minimum EVM requirements for each downlink modulation scheme, while Fig. 6-48 has a sample measurement with a signal analyzer.

Modulation scheme for PDSCH	Required EVM [%]
QPSK	17.5
16QAM	12.5
64QAM	8

Fig. 6-47 EVM minimum requirements.

Source: [3GPP TS 36.104, Ref. 25], reproduced by permission of 3GPP

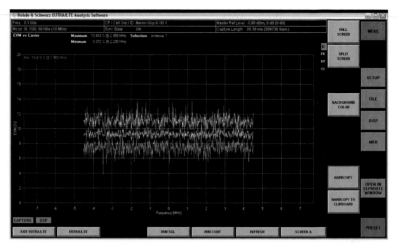

Fig. 6-48 EVM measurement on an LTE downlink signal (minimum, average and peak measurement traces)

Time alignment between transmitter branches (test 6.3.3)

The time alignment between transmitter branches is a measurement that is important in base stations that support transmit diversity or spatial multiplexing. The signals that are transmitted by two or more antennas must exhibit time alignment. Thus, the time alignment error in transmit diversity and spatial multiplexing is specified as the delay between the signals from two antennas at the antenna ports. The time alignment error shall be less than 65 ns (minimum requirement).

DL RS power (test 6.5.4)

The downlink reference symbol power is the resource element power of downlink reference symbols. The base station signals the absolute downlink reference symbol power to the terminal (RRC parameter *referenceSignalPower* e.g. in *SystemInformationBlockType2*). This test verifies the accuracy of this indication in terms of the maximum deviation between the signaled DL RS power and the actual DL RS power at the base station antenna connector. The DL RS power shall be within ±2.1 dB of the DL RS power indicated by the base station (minimum requirement).

As was the case in terminal testing, measurements of **unwanted emissions** from the transmitter are extremely important in base station testing as well. These measurements ensure that the base station transmitter does not cause unwanted effects that can impair co-existence with other entities and networks in real operation. For the base station test, unwanted emissions are classified as before as either "out-of-band emissions" immediately outside the channel bandwidth or "spurious emissions" beyond that range.

6.3.1.5 Unwanted emissions

Occupied bandwidth (test 6.6.1)

There is, moreover, a requirement for occupied bandwidth which is to verify that the emissions from the base station do not occupy excessive bandwidth. The occupied bandwidth comprises 99 % of the total mean transmit power and shall be less than the specified LTE channel bandwidth.

The out-of-band emissions requirement for the base station transmitter is specified both in terms of the **adjacent channel leakage power ratio (ACLR)** and the **operating band unwanted emissions**.

Adjacent channel leakage power ratio (test 6.6.2)

The ACLR measurement determines the ratio of the filtered mean power on the assigned channel frequency to the filtered mean power on the adjacent channel frequency. As the adjacent channels, both LTE and UTRA carriers have been assumed for deriving the requirement. The ACLR value shall not exceed 45 dB (minimum requirement) for all of the cases specified, and for FDD and TDD. Besides this relative requirement, an absolute requirement of –13 dBm/MHz / –15 dBm/MHz (category A / B, respectively) is specified. The less stringent requirement applies.

A sample ACLR measurement performed with a signal analyzer is shown in Fig. 6-49.

Operating band unwanted emissions test (test 6.6.3)

The operating band unwanted emissions are defined for a frequency range ±10 MHz from the operating band edges. 3GPP TS 36.141 provides different requirements depending on the channel bandwidth as well as different regional requirements. Fig. 6-50 shows a sample measurement for a 10 MHz FDD signal.

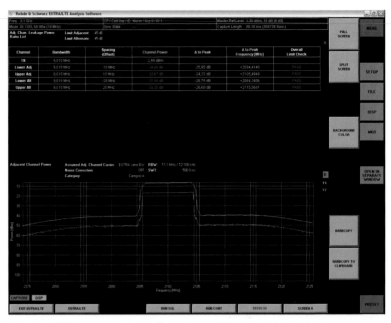

Fig. 6-49 ACLR measurement performed on an LTE downlink signal.

Fig. 6-50 Measurement of operating band unwanted emissions.

Transmitter spurious emissions (test 6.6.4)

The test of transmitter spurious emissions relates to the frequency range from 9 kHz to 12.75 GHz, excluding the frequency range from 10 MHz below the lowest frequency of the downlink operating band up to 10 MHz above the highest frequency of the downlink operating band. Different measurement bandwidths are defined for different frequency ranges. Additional requirements apply for base station spurious emissions in order to protect the base station receiver in the case of FDD operation and ensure co-existence with other systems in the same geographical area.

6.3.1.6 Transmitter intermodulation (test 6.7)

The transmitter intermodulation requirement is a measure of the capability of the transmitter to inhibit the generation of signals in its non-linear elements due to the presence of the transmitter's own transmit signal and an interfering signal that reaches the transmitter via the antenna. The transmit intermodulation level is the power of the intermodulation products when an E-UTRA signal with a channel bandwidth of 5 MHz is injected as an interfering signal into an antenna connector at a mean power level that is 30 dB lower than that of the mean power of the wanted signal. The test setup is shown in Fig. 6-51.

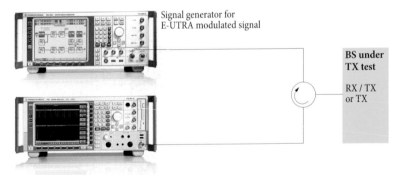

Signal generator for
E-UTRA modulated signal

BS under
TX test

RX / TX
or TX

Fig. 6-51 Test setup for transmitter intermodulation measurements

147

6.3.2 Receiver characteristics

Fig. 6-52 provides an overview of the receiver tests specified in 3GPP TS 36.141 [Ref. 24].

ı Reference sensitivity level
ı Dynamic range
ı In-channel selectivity
ı Adjacent channel selectivity (ACS) and narrow-band blocking
ı Blocking
ı Receiver spurious emissions
ı Receiver intermodulation

Fig. 6-52 LTE base station receiver tests

Receiver characteristics are verified based on uplink fixed reference measurement channels which exactly describe the configuration of the uplink LTE signal used for a certain test.

A sample set of fixed reference channels used for reference sensitivity and in-channel selectivity tests is shown in Fig. 6-53. Different fixed reference channels are defined for other test cases.

Reference channel	A1-1	A1-2	A1-3	A1-4	A1-5
Allocated resource blocks	6	15	25	3	9
DFT-OFDM Symbols per subframe	12	12	12	12	12
Modulation	QPSK	QPSK	QPSK	QPSK	QPSK
Code rate	1/3	1/3	1/3	1/3	1/3
Payload size (bit)	600	1544	2216	256	936
Transport block CRC (bit)	24	24	24	24	24
Code block CRC size (bit)	0	0	0	0	0
Number of code blocks – C	1	1	1	1	1
Coded block size including 12-bit trellis termination (bit)	1884	4716	6732	852	2892
Total number of bits per subframe	1728	4320	7200	864	2592
Total symbols per subframe	864	2160	3600	432	1296

Fig. 6-53 Fixed reference channels for reference sensitivity and in-channel selectivity.

Source: [3GPP TS 36.141, Ref. 24], reproduced by permission of 3GPP

The LTE coding chain is illustrated in Fig. 6-54 in more detail to help explain the terminology used in Fig. 6-53.

Example: A1-1

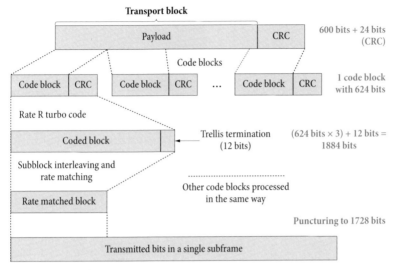

Fig. 6-54 LTE coding chain.

Source: [3GPP TS 36.141, Ref. 24], reproduced by permission of 3GPP

First, a cyclic redundancy check (CRC) is attached to the payload data packet to be transmitted in a subframe. Larger packets will be segmented into different code blocks, each with its own additional CRC. Each code block is turbo encoded. Rate matching is performed to fit the available bits on the physical layer.

6.3.2.1 Reference sensitivity level (test 7.2)

Now let us have a closer look at the different receiver tests from [Ref. 24]. The reference sensitivity power level is the minimum mean receive power that still makes it possible to provide ≥ 95 % throughput compared to the maximum throughput that would be possible with the fixed reference channel used for the test. Each receive port of the base station is tested separately. The test setup for measuring reference sensitivity level is shown in Fig. 6-55. A signal generator provides the uplink fixed reference channel in accordance with the parameters specified and the achieved throughput is measured on base station side.

RF signal generator, e. g. R&S®SMU 200 A,
providing fixed reference channel

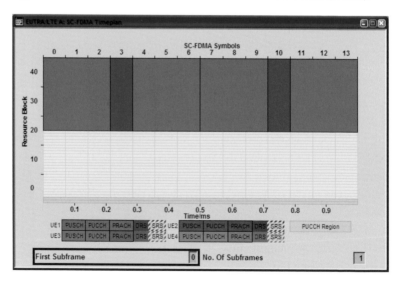

Fig. 6-55 Test setup for base station receiver measurement (reference sensitivity level).

Example: For a 10 MHz LTE signal, FRC A1-3 from Fig. 6-53 is used for the reference sensitivity level test. The maximum throughput achievable with this FRC equals the payload size × the number of uplink subframes per second, i. e. 2216 bit × 1000/s = 2.216 Mbit/s. The specified reference sensitivity level is –101.5 dBm (minimum requirement) in this case. At this receive power level, throughput must always be ≥ 95 % of 2.216 Mbit/s. Note that the FRC A1-3 consists of only 25 resource blocks while the 10 MHz LTE bandwidth spans 50 resource blocks. The requirement for the reference sensitivity level must be fulfilled for each consecutive application of a single instance of FRC A1-3 mapped to disjoint frequency ranges with a width of 25 resource blocks each. This is illustrated in Fig. 6-56 with the time / frequency diagram for the uplink signal. One subframe of 1 ms is shown in the time domain (x-axis).

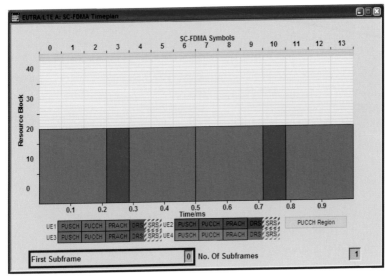

Fig. 6-56 Mapping FRC A1-3 to disjoint frequency ranges (reference sensitivity criterion must be fulfilled for both).

6.3.2.2 Dynamic range (test 7.3)

The dynamic range is a measure of the receiver's capability to receive a wanted signal in the presence of an interfering AWGN signal inside the received channel bandwidth. The test setup is similar to Fig. 6-55, but the signal generator now adds noise to the wanted signal. As before, a throughput requirement of ≥ 95 % must be fulfilled for a specified reference measurement channel (FRCs A2-1 to A2-3 are used for this test) and at a specified wanted signal mean power and interfering signal mean power.

6.3.2.3 In-channel selectivity (test 7.4)

The in-channel selectivity is a measure of the receiver's ability to suppress IQ leakage when receiving a wanted signal at its assigned resource blocks in the presence of an interfering LTE uplink signal with a larger power spectral density. The wanted signal is situated on one side of DC and the interfering signal is adjacent on the opposite side of DC. Fig. 6-57 shows the placement of the wanted and interfering signals around DC as an example for a channel bandwidth of 1.4 MHz. In this scenario, the throughput must be ≥ 95 % of the maximum possible throughput of the FRC.

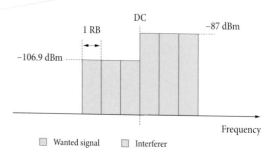

Fig. 6-57 Positioning of wanted signal and interferer for measuring in-channel selectivity (1.4 MHz channel bandwidth example, minimum requirement).

6.3.2.4 Adjacent channel selectivity and narrow-band blocking (test 7.5)

The adjacent channel selectivity (ACS) is a measure of the receiver's ability to suppress interfering signals in the channels adjacent to the wanted signal. The interfering signal is a QPSK-modulated LTE uplink signal. The test setup is shown in Fig. 6-58.

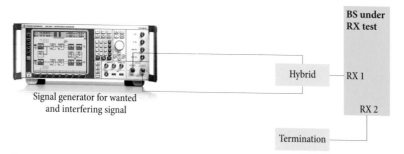

Fig. 6-58 Setup for adjacent channel selectivity and narrow-band blocking.

A sample signal configuration for the 10 MHz channel bandwidth case is given in Fig. 6-59.

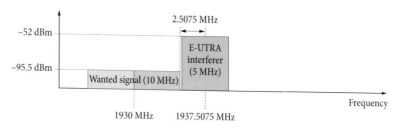

Fig. 6-59 Sample signal configuration for ACS measurement (10 MHz LTE signal at 1930 MHz, minimum requirement).

Narrow-band blocking is a related test with a similar objective to ACS, but with an interfering signal that consists of one QPSK-modulated resource block where the offset between this resource block and the channel edge of the wanted signal is variable.

Throughput for both tests must not fall below 95 % of the maximum FRC throughput.

6.3.2.5 Blocking (test 7.6)

The blocking test provides a measure of the receiver's ability to receive a wanted signal on its assigned channel in the presence of an unwanted interferer, which is either a 1.4 MHz, 3 MHz or 5 MHz LTE uplink signal for in band blocking near the operating frequency band, or a CW signal for out-of-band blocking. The interfering signal lies between 1 MHz and 12.75 GHz and is swept with a step size of 1 MHz. The test criterion is the achievable throughput. A sample interferer setup is shown in Fig. 6-60. The interfering signal's minimum offset to the right channel edge of the wanted signal is indicated. From here, the interfering signal is swept up to a frequency of 2 GHz (= operating band 1 upper edge + 20 MHz). Beyond this point, a CW carrier is used as the interfering signal up to 12.75 GHz.

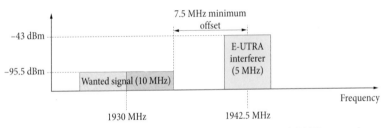

Fig. 6-60 Sample signal configuration for blocking measurement (10 MHz wanted LTE signal at 1930 MHz, minimum requirement).

When LTE base stations are co-located with GSM, UMTS or LTE base stations operating in a different frequency band, additional blocking requirements apply which are evaluated using a CW signal as the interferer.

6.3.2.6 Receiver spurious emissions (test 7.7)

The spurious emissions power is the power of emissions generated or amplified in a receiver that appear at the base station receiver antenna connector. The requirements apply to all base stations with separate RX and TX antenna ports. The test must be performed when both TX and RX are on and with the TX port terminated. In the case of TDD base stations with a common RX and TX antenna port, the requirement applies during the transmitter OFF period. In the case of FDD base stations with a common RX and TX antenna port, the transmitter spurious emission requirement applies. As a minimum requirement, the tolerated level of spurious emissions is specified as a value of –57 dBm for the frequency range 30 MHz to 1 GHz (100 kHz measurement bandwidth) and –47 dBm for the frequency range 1 GHz to 12.75 GHz (1 MHz measurement bandwidth).

6.3.2.7 Receiver intermodulation (test 7.8)

The receiver intermodulation response rejection is a measure of the receiver's ability to inhibit generation of intermodulation products in its nonlinear elements and receive a wanted signal in the presence of two interfering signals which have a specific frequency relationship to the wanted signal. Third and higher-order mixing of the two interfering signals produces an interfering signal in the band of the wanted signal. Throughput in this scenario must not fall below 95 % of the maximum FRC throughput.

Example: For a 10 MHz LTE signal, the interfering signals are a CW signal with a 7.5 MHz offset from the channel edge of the wanted signal and a 5 MHz LTE signal with 17.7 MHz offset; see Fig. 6-61.

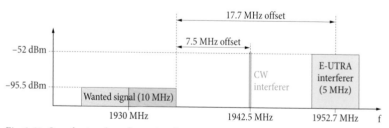

Fig. 6-61 Sample signal configuration for receiver intermodulation (10 MHz wanted LTE signal at 1930 MHz, minimum requirement).

Additional requirements apply to the narrow-band case in which an interfering LTE signal with only 1 RB is used.

6.3.3 Performance requirements

Base station performance tests are particularly important in LTE because they verify the performance of the complex layer 1 features such as the HARQ retransmission protocol, uplink timing adjustment and uplink control information reporting. Fig. 6-62 gives an overview of the performance tests specified in [Ref. 24].

- PUSCH performance in multipath fading conditions
- High speed train conditions (optional)
- Uplink timing adjustment
- HARQ-ACK multiplexed on PUSCH
- ACK missed detection for single user PUCCH format 1a
- CQI missed detection for PUCCH format 2
- ACK missed detection for multi-user PUCCH format 1a
- PRACH false alarm probability and missed detection

Fig. 6-62 LTE base station performance tests.

6.3.3.1 Performance requirements for PUSCH (test 8.2.1)

For verifying the PUSCH performance of the base station receiver, the minimum required throughput for a given signal-to-noise ratio is the key criterion. As in the receiver tests, fixed reference channels (FRCs) are defined as a baseline for verifying performance requirements which stipulate the exact uplink resource allocation and parameter set. As an example, the FRCs for QPSK modulation are shown in Fig. 6-63. Similar tables exist for 16QAM and 64QAM. The fixed reference channels for QPSK are named A3-1 to A3-7 and differ in terms of the number of resource blocks allocated. The fixed reference channels for 16QAM are referred to as A4-1 to A4-8 and those for 64QAM as A5-1 to A5-7.

Reference channel	A3-1	A3-2	A3-3	A3-4	A3-5	A3-6	A3-7
Allocated resource blocks	1	6	15	25	50	75	100
DFT-OFDM symbols per subframe	12	12	12	12	12	12	12
Modulation	QPSK	QPSK	QPSK	QPSK	QPSK	QPSK	QPSK
Code rate	1/3	1/3	1/3	1/3	1/3	1/3	1/3
Payload size (bit)	104	600	1544	2216	5160	6712	10296
Transport block CRC (bit)	24	24	24	24	24	24	24
Code block CRC size (bit)	0	0	0	0	0	24	24
Number of code blocks – C	1	1	1	1	1	2	2
Coded block size including 12-bit trellis termination (bit)	396	1884	4716	6732	15564	10188	15564
Total number of bits per subframe	288	1728	4320	7200	14400	21600	28800
Total symbols per subframe	144	864	2160	3600	7200	10800	14400

Fig. 6-63 FRC parameters for performance requirements (QPSK).

Source: [3GPP TS 36.141, Ref. 24], reproduced by permission of 3GPP

Again like the receiver tests, the required throughput as a performance criterion is expressed as a fraction of the maximum achievable throughput of the FRC that is selected for the test. The maximum throughput for an FRC equals the payload size × the number of uplink subframes per second (= 1000 for FDD). For example, for A3-7 a maximum throughput of 10296 × 1000 bit/s = 10.3 Mbit/s can be achieved.

HARQ retransmissions need to be considered to determine the realistic throughput. Thus, for verifying base station performance, a closed loop test setup is required that takes into account ACK / NACK feedback; see Fig. 6-64 for the basic principle. Modern signal generators can provide everything needed to perform such a closed loop test in a single box. The base station is the device under test and receives a PUSCH FRC signal over the air that is generated by a signal generator. The signal generator thus simulates the activities of the terminal. HARQ ACK / NACK feedback in response to the PUSCH is provided by the base station under test via a direct feedback line to the signal generator. The signal generator evaluates the feedback and sends new transmissions or retransmissions of data packets. For retransmissions, the redundancy version can also be adapted, just as in real operation. The fading simulator that is part of the signal generator provides the required multipath fading conditions and the required AWGN can also be added to the signal.

Fig. 6-64 Test setup for uplink performance tests including HARQ feedback.

The performance tests must be performed for many different scenarios and parameter combinations, i. e. for all supported bandwidths and modulation schemes and for different multipath fading and signal-to-noise ratio (SNR) conditions, as required by [Ref. 24]. For example, the test requirements for the 10 MHz bandwidth scenario are captured in Fig. 6-65.

Cyclic prefix	Propagation conditions	FRC	Fraction of maximum throughput	SNR (dB)
Normal	EPA 5 Hz	A3-5	30 %	−3.6
			70 %	0.2
		A4-6	70 %	11.4
		A5-5	70 %	18.9
	EVA 5 Hz	A3-1	30 %	−2.1
			70 %	2.5
		A4-1	30 %	4.9
			70 %	12.0
		A5-1	70 %	19.4
	EVA 70 Hz	A3-5	30 %	−3.5
			70 %	0.7
		A4-6	30 %	5.1
			70 %	13.2
	ETU 70 Hz	A3-1	30 %	−1.9
			70 %	3.0
	ETU 300 Hz	A3-1	30 %	−1.6
			70 %	3.5
Extended	ETU 70 Hz	A4-2	30 %	5.4
			70 %	14.2

Fig. 6-65 Test requirements for PUSCH, 10 MHz channel bandwidth, 2 RX antennas.

Source: [3GPP TS 36.141, Ref. 24], reproduced by permission of 3GPP

Note: Propagation conditions are discussed in more detail in 6.4, page 154. EPA 5 Hz refers to multipath propagation conditions in accordance with the Extended Pedestrian A model with a maximum

Doppler frequency of 5 Hz. EVA 70 Hz refers to multipath propagation conditions in accordance with the Extended Vehicular A model with a maximum Doppler frequency of 70 Hz. ETU 70 Hz / ETU 300 Hz refers to multipath propagation conditions in accordance with the Extended Typical Urban model with a maximum Doppler frequency of 70 Hz / 300 Hz.

6.3.3.2 Performance requirements for High Speed Train conditions (test 8.2.4)

An optional test addresses base station performance requirements for high speed train (HST) conditions, verifying the FRC throughput for special propagation conditions (so-called HST scenarios), simulating velocities up to 350 km/h.

6.3.3.3 Performance requirements for UL timing adjustment (test 8.2.2)

The performance requirements for uplink timing adjustment are determined based on two (simulated) terminals, one moving (= wanted signal) and the other stationary. It is verified that the base station receiver performance is not degraded due to the presence of the second terminal and insufficient timing adjustment by the base station. Specific fixed reference channels are defined for this test. Once again, the performance is measured in terms of throughput and HARQ retransmissions are required. Therefore, this test also requires a closed loop test setup; see Fig. 6-66. Receiver diversity conditions are assumed. Besides the HARQ feedback, uplink timing adjustment feedback is required. Depending on the requested time shifts, the signal generator delays or advances the uplink signal of the first terminal in realtime. The screenshot of the signal generator illustrates simulation of the signals for the two terminals and shows the different stages in the signal generation chain. The moving propagation conditions as required by the test, including the speed of the moving terminal, can be selected in the fading simulator.

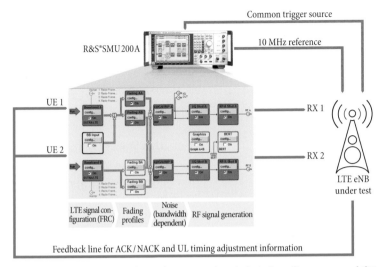

Fig. 6-66 Test setup for verifying a base station's uplink timing adjustment capabilities.

The performance of the uplink control information signaling reception must be tested in detail and is covered by several tests. Correct ACK / NACK reception by the base station is verified based on two parameters: Probability of detection of ACK and probability of false detection of ACK. The fraction of correctly detected ACKs must be larger than 99 % for the specified SNR conditions and the fraction of falsely detected ACKs must be less than 1 %.

6.3.3.4 Performance requirements for HARQ-ACK multiplexed on PUSCH (test 8.2.3)

The performance requirement for HARQ-ACK multiplexed on PUSCH verifies whether the base station is able to correctly detect HARQ ACK / NACK messages within the PUSCH. For the test setup, a signal generator is used to provide a test signal including the PUSCH with data only transmission and the PUSCH with ACK information. During the test, the following statistics are maintained: The number of ACKs detected during data only transmissions and the number of missed ACKs during the PUSCH with ACK transmission.

6.3.3.5 ACK missed detection for single user PUCCH format 1a (test 8.3.1)

The corresponding test ACK missed detection for single user PUCCH format 1a is based on the same principle, but it verifies the reception of ACK / NACK via the PUCCH. In this case, the test signal consists of a pattern containing both PUCCH transmissions with ACK and transmission pauses.

6.3.3.6 ACK missed detection for multi-user PUCCH format 1a (test 8.3.3)

This test is extended further by the performance requirement for ACK missed detection for multi-user PUCCH format 1a. Four signals are configured for testing the base station receiver: One wanted signal and three interferers. The test setup for this test is thus more complex. Fig. 6-67 shows an example with two signal generators, each of which provides the signals representing two terminals. The first generator simulates the tested wanted signal and interferer 1, the second generator simulates interferers 2 and 3.

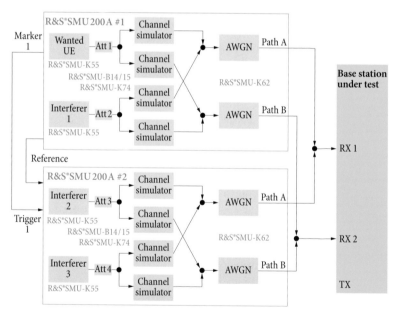

Fig. 6-67 Test setup for multi-user PUCCH performance verification.

Source: based on [3GPP TS 36.141, Ref. 24], reproduced by permission of 3GPP

6.3.3.7 CQI missed detection for PUCCH format 2
(test 8.3.2)

Not only ACK / NACK detection, but also correct CQI detection is verified. The performance requirement for CQI missed detection for PUCCH format 2 is determined by the probability of detection of CQI. The fraction of falsely detected CQIs shall be less than 1 % and the fraction of correctly detected CQIs shall be larger than 99 % for the defined SNR values. The signal generator sends a test pattern with CQI transmissions on PUCCH format 2 separated by transmission pauses.

6.3.3.8 PRACH false alarm probability and missed detection
(test 8.4.1)

The performance requirements for the PRACH channel are given by PRACH false alarm probability and missed detection. The performance requirement for the PRACH for preamble detection is determined by two parameters: Probability of detection of the preamble (Pd) and probability of false detection of the preamble (Pfa) when input to the base station receiver is only noise. The performance is measured for the required SNR at a probability of detection Pd of 99 %. Possible failures may involve detecting a different preamble than the one that was sent, not detecting a preamble at all, or correct preamble detection but with the wrong timing estimation. The Pfa must be 0.1 % or less.

6.4 LTE MIMO verification and channel models

The previous chapters showed that MIMO multi antenna technology heavily influences the test requirements for base stations and terminals. This is especially true in the terminal performance tests which are specified for different MIMO modes and configurations; see 6.2.3, page 127. But even beyond these specific requirements stipulated by 3GPP, MIMO verification is an important testing area for LTE-capable components, terminals and base stations.

Testing of MIMO technology represents a special challenge due to the complexity and various design and verification issues associated with MIMO, affecting not only the RF, but also all of the protocol layers from the physical layer up to the application layer. On both the base station and terminal ends, transmit and receive chains and antenna ports must be verified thoroughly. MIMO signal processing must be tested both from a functional and a performance point of view, considering especially the high throughput that can be achieved with MIMO which entails special handling by the protocol architecture. Furthermore, multiple antenna systems impose new constraints on the layout of chipsets and terminals. Another aspect to be investigated is the processing power requirements and battery consumption of the new algorithms. Beamforming puts additional requirements on the antenna architecture and operation on the base station end.

Fig. 6-68 shows an example of a MIMO test setup for a terminal receiver test. The signal generator simulates an LTE MIMO base station signal as the stimulus for the receiver. For a 2 × 2 system, it is necessary to generate two baseband signals and two RF signals for two different transmit antennas. Fading simulators included in the signal generator provide the MIMO-specific propagation conditions.

Vector signal generator R&S®SMU 200 A

MIMO device
under test

Fig. 6-68   MIMO test setup for terminal receiver test including fading channel simulation. The R&S®SMU 200 A vector signal generator provides LTE downlink signals from 2 TX antennas (including MIMO channel simulation).

As shown in 6.2.3, page 127, terminal performance tests are repeated under different propagation conditions. This enables accurate modeling of realistic radio channel conditions including typical effects such as path loss, multipath fading and Doppler. Not only for conformance tests, but also during early R&D work, fading simulation is important in order to evaluate the performance of terminals and base stations.

While simulation of propagation conditions should naturally be as realistic as possible, the required simulation and testing times must also be kept in mind. Complex models that, say, incorporate stochastic modeling of radio channel parameters are therefore not necessarily the best choice for mobile radio R&D and conformance testing.

Fading channel models for SISO systems have been in use for many years, e.g. the channel models for the GSM and UMTS/WCDMA standards. GSM defined three propagation models: Typical urban, hilly terrain and rural area. UMTS/WCDMA channel models are derived from the ITU channel models indoor, pedestrian and vehicular. All of these channel models reflect the propagation conditions in different environments by modeling the expected impact of the environment on the propagation. The ITU channel models are based on a classical tapped delay line channel model and e.g. differ in the number and distribution of fading paths and delay spread of the channel. Fig. 6-69 shows the example of a GSM typical urban TU50 model (the "50" refers to the modeled terminal velocity of 50 km/h) with 6 paths. The y-axis shows the path loss of each path and the x-axis shows the delay of the path in µs. In this example, a Rayleigh distribution is used for modeling the amplitude of the paths (Rayleigh fading assumes that no line of sight path is present). The time-variant behavior is a classical Doppler spectrum.

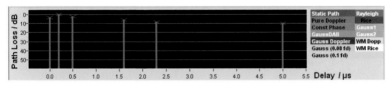

Fig. 6-69 Tapped delay line model.

While most channel models rely on a fixed distribution of paths, dynamic scenarios are also available, e.g. birth-death and moving propagation models as used in UMTS/WCDMA.

The ITU channel models for UMTS/WCDMA had to be extended by 3GPP release 8 for LTE. This is due in part to certain drawbacks exhibited by UMTS/WCDMA channel models for modeling high bandwidth systems due to their periodicity in the frequency correlation function. Thus, in the LTE channel models, the higher bandwidths of up to 20 MHz had to be taken into account (compared to 5 MHz bandwidth operation in UMTS/WCDMA). Furthermore, the UMTS/WCDMA channel models were designed for SISO only. For LTE, MIMO scenarios had to be considered additionally.

Instead of characterizing the radio channel between one transmit and one receive antenna as in a SISO system, the channels between each of the Nt transmit antennas and each of the Nr receive antennas must be modeled separately in a multi antenna system. In a 2 × 2 system, four separate channels must therefore be modeled independently. Since the assumption of uncorrelated fading processes on the different channels would be too optimistic, the correlation parameters must be reflected as well. Extension of the existing ITU models and inclusion of spatial correlation models were considered by 3GPP to represent a reasonable approach in terms of the complexity and performance.

Modern signal generators allow inclusion of baseband fading simulation, including predefined channel models for SISO and MIMO for the different standards. This is a significant advantage especially in the area of MIMO testing. Fig. 6-70 shows the user interface of a signal generator for a 2 × 2 MIMO receiver test setup including realtime fading. The signal generator not only provides the LTE baseband signals, but also has the ability to add fading and noise to the signals.

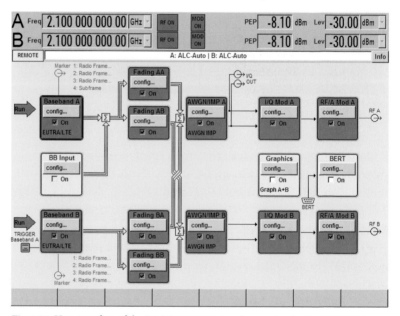

Fig. 6-70 User interface of the R&S®SMU 200 A signal generator for 2 × 2 MIMO tests: The signal flow is shown from the generation of the two baseband LTE signals on the left via the four fading channels to the two RF outputs on the right.

For terminal receiver testing, the signal generator provides the baseband signals for two base station transmit antennas. The baseband signal can be configured flexibly. Transmit diversity, cyclic delay diversity and spatial multiplexing can be selected and configured. Four baseband fading simulators provide the fading characteristics for the channels between each transmit and each receive antenna. Correlation properties can be set individually. For full flexibility, it is possible to specify the full (NtNr) × (NtNr) correlation matrix for each path (Fig. 6-71). It is also possible to use a simplified model and specify only complex correlation coefficients for the transmitter and receiver ends. The faded signals are then summed up correctly before RF conversion and provided to the two RF outputs which can be connected to the dual antenna terminal.

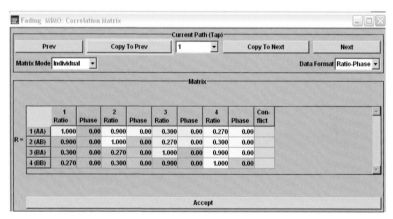

Fig. 6-71 Setting the 4 × 4 correlation matrix for a 2 × 2 MIMO test setup in a fading simulator.

Multipath fading propagation conditions for LTE conformance testing purposes are specified in 3GPP TS 36.141 (base station testing, Ref. 24) and 3GPP TS 36.521 (terminal testing, Ref. 22). Three basic channel models are defined:

ı Extended Pedestrian (EPA)
ı Extended Vehicular A model (EVA)
ı Extended Typical Urban model (ETU)

Their basic characteristics are shown in Fig. 6-72.

Model	Number of channel taps	Delay spread (r.m.s.)	Maximum excess tap delay (span)
Extended Pedestrian A (EPA)	7	45 ns	410 ns
Extended Vehicular A model (EVA)	9	357 ns	2510 ns
Extended Typical Urban model (ETU)	9	991 ns	5000 ns

Fig. 6-72 Delay profiles for LTE channel models.

Source: [3GPP TS 36.521, Ref. 22], reproduced by permission of 3GPP

3GPP TS 36.521 for terminal testing [Ref. 22] additionally contains pre-defined MIMO channel correlation matrices. High, medium and low correlation models are provided.

Based on the test setups described in this chapter, extensions are possible to cover additional test needs. For example, the test setup in Fig. 6-68 can be expanded to cover a system with four transmit antennas by using a second signal generator. Another typical test setup is the combination of a radio communication tester for terminal testing plus a signal generator with fading capabilities; see Fig. 93

Fig. 6-73 Combination of radio communication tester and fading simulator for terminal testing.

The downlink signal provided by the radio communication tester is faded by the signal generator and then connected to the terminal. This setup enables evaluation of the throughput and application performance including MIMO and full signaling functionality under realistic propagation conditions. This setup is also used to verify whether the terminal's MIMO implementation is able to provide the desired maximum throughput. Different types of applications can be evaluated. Note that the tests that can be performed with such a setup go far beyond the test coverage provided by 3GPP and thus allows manufacturers and network operators to evaluate terminal performance in accordance with individual use cases and assumptions.

For MIMO **transmitter tests**, i.e. base station transmitters in the downlink, signal analyzers are used. First of all, the typical SISO transmitter measurements are carried out to make sure the transmit chain fulfills the requirements on output power, frequency error, RF spectrum emissions and modulation accuracy. These measurements can be performed with a signal analyzer for each antenna separately. Usually, each MIMO antenna port transmits a different pilot pattern so the receiver is able to distinguish the antenna signals and make the channel estimation.

This is illustrated in Fig. 6-74 with a screenshot of an LTE signal analyzer solution. In this example, the correct antenna is selected for signal analysis.

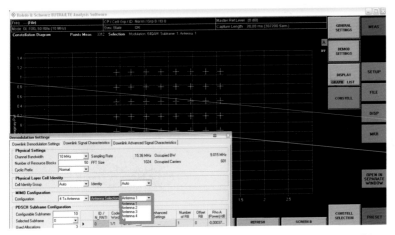

Fig. 6-74   Screenshot of the Rohde & Schwarz LTE signal analysis software: One of the four transmit antennas is selected to prepare for the RF measurements. In the background, a constellation diagram for the LTE downlink signal with a 64QAM modulation scheme is shown.

Depending on the type of MIMO precoding, one signal analyzer may still be sufficient to investigate each transmit antenna's signal separately. For more complex types of MIMO precoding for spatial multiplexing, however, two or more signal analyzers have to be connected to collect and process measurement results for all of the transmit antennas. One signal analyzer functions as the master and the others as slaves. Such a test setup for the 2 × 2 MIMO case is shown in Fig. 6-75. The signal is MIMO-precoded, e.g. for spatial multiplexing, so this precoding needs to be reversed by the signal analyzers to obtain the original data streams and analyze each stream separately. Analysis of precoded LTE MIMO signals from four transmit antennas is possible with a similar approach using four signal analyzers.

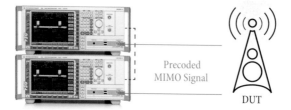

Precoded MIMO Signal

DUT

Fig. 6-75 Test setup for 2 × 2 MIMO transmitter testing.

Fig. 6-76 shows a composite constellation diagram that was measured with the setup in Fig. 6-75 prior to reversion of the MIMO precoding. Only after reversion of the precoding can each stream be analyzed separately, e.g. in terms of modulation quality using the information from both signal analyzers.

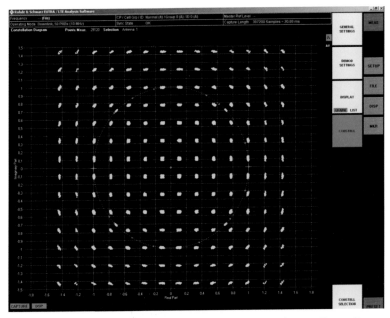

Fig. 6-76 LTE MIMO signal captured with two analyzers: Sample constellation diagram before reversion of the precoding.

Use of beamforming (transmission mode 7) in LTE leads to additional test and measurement challenges. Adaptive beamforming algorithms are designed to adapt the antenna beams continuously so the receiver performance is optimized. Beamforming is especially important for TD-LTE since the reciprocity of the radio channel in the downlink and uplink in a TDD system makes it possible to design a beamforming algorithm that does not require explicit feedback signaling from the terminal. The results from the uplink channel estimation can be processed to derive the beamforming weights for the different antenna elements for downlink transmission.

For transmit beamforming, one must verify whether the mobile station receiver is able to handle the reception of user-specific reference symbols, and the receiver performance for different modulation and coding schemes and test channel conditions including AWGN and fading must be tested. This is taken into account by a PDSCH demodulation performance test in 3GPP TS 36.521 [Ref. 22]; see 6.2.3, page 127. Furthermore, the base station performance for transmit and / or receive beamforming has to be tested and correct signaling of user-specific reference symbols needs to be verified. The beamforming algorithm typically requires a well-calibrated antenna system with a defined phase relation between the individual antenna elements of the setup for each operating frequency. Characterization of the base station antenna is typically performed with a vector network analyzer that provides an exact characterization of the phase relations. A sample measurement setup is shown in Fig. 6-77. The switch unit makes it possible to select the antenna elements under test which are then evaluated by the vector network analyzer.

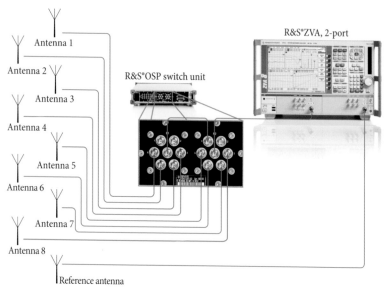

Fig. 6-77 Characterizing an antenna structure with several elements by means of a network analyzer in combination with a switch unit.

6.5 Protocol tests for terminals

Verifying the signaling functionality of the terminal is of crucial importance in all stages of terminal testing ranging from early R&D and conformance testing through manufacturing and service. Verification encompasses the full protocol stack from layer 1 up to the user plane and applications and may also include parallel RF parametric tests. For signaling tests, a radio communication tester (see Fig. 6-3) is used that can be configured for the specific test objective. It acts as a base station simulator to test the connected wireless device under test which can be a chipset or complete handset. The connection can be provided via the RF interface or digital IQ interface, alternatively. Testing via the digital IQ interface is required in case the RF section of the chipset has not yet been integrated such that baseband functionality needs to be tested separately.

Each protocol layer must be tested in detail: LTE layer 1 has significant functionality requiring quick downlink and uplink interaction. This includes layer 1 procedures such as cell search, hybrid ARQ retransmission protocol, scheduling, link adaptation, uplink timing control and power control, to name a few examples. These procedures have stringent timing requirements and thorough testing of layer 1 procedures is needed to guarantee LTE performance.

Layer 2 testing addresses correct operation and performance of the MAC, RLC and PDCP protocols. On layer 3, signaling functionality such as call setup and release, call reconfigurations, state handling, measurement configuration / reporting and mobility are important testing areas. Interworking with 2G and 3G systems such as GSM/EDGE, WCDMA/HSPA and CDMA2000® 1xRTT/1x-EV-DO is a requirement for LTE and needs to be tested thoroughly. For user plane and application testing, special focus is placed on verification of throughput requirements in order to make sure that the terminal protocol stack and applications are capable of handling high data rates. Different services need to be tested on an end-to-end basis to verify the quality of service of, say, video streaming, FTP downloads or voice over IP. Flexible test scenarios with individual parameterization are needed for R&D purposes starting at a very early stage in LTE implementation work. These R&D test scenarios are typically tailored to meet early testing needs.

Beyond R&D, 3GPP defines a complete range of signaling tests. These are defined in specification 3GPP TS 36.523-1 [Ref. 26] in prose and serve as the basis for protocol conformance tests and certification. The tests stipulated in 3GPP TS 36.523-1 [Ref. 26] are organized into different sections based on the protocol layers and functionalities, e.g. tests on idle mode operation, layer 2 (MAC, RLC, PDCP), RRC, EPS mobility management, EPS session management, etc. These tests address not only the behavior of the terminal in an LTE-only network, but also the interaction with legacy 2G and 3G technologies and the mobility between LTE and these technologies. The tests stipulated by 3GPP are strongly oriented towards correct functioning of the LTE protocol in order to verify the behavior of a particular protocol layer or a function within that layer.

By way of example, Fig. 6-78 shows an excerpt from the layer 2 / MAC test cases specified in 36.523-1 [Ref. 26], or more specifically, the test cases for DL-SCH data transfer only. For each test, the test conditions, message content and expected terminal behavior is clearly specified.

7.1.3.1	Correct handling of DL assignment / dynamic case
7.1.3.2	Correct handling of DL assignment: semi persistent case
7.1.3.3	MAC PDU header handling
7.1.3.4	Correct HARQ process handling [DCCH / DTCH]
7.1.3.5	Correct HARQ process handling [CCCH]
7.1.3.6	Correct HARQ process handling [BCCH]
7.1.3.7	MAC padding
7.1.3.9	MAC reset-DL

Fig. 6-78 MAC test cases for DL-SCH data transfer.

Manufacturers of chipsets and terminals as well as network operators typically have test requirements that exceed the coverage provided by 3GPP. These requirements are driven more by the need to verify terminal behavior in realistic scenarios and to prepare interoperability tests using live base stations and networks of different manufacturers. Thus, a wide range of test cases is needed to address real network scenarios. This also includes end-to-end scenarios with real applications in order to verify the subscriber's experience. Terminal manufacturers seek to identify implementation errors in the chipset or terminal as early as possible since errors that are identified later in a field trial or even in commercial use can generate significant costs and delay the introduction of new products.

Thus, for signaling tests it is typically an important requirement to have a highly flexible programming interface available on the tester platform in order to allow individual adaptation of test cases in accordance with the customer's needs. Furthermore, individual parameterization of test cases is an important requirement. Fig. 6-79 shows a screenshot of a message composer tool that allows adaptation of the information elements in an RRC message that the tester is expected to send to the terminal under test.

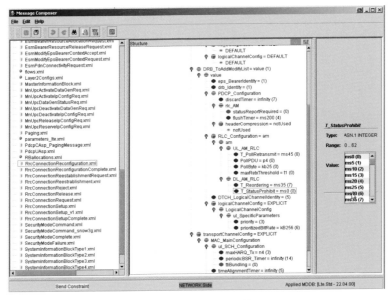

Fig. 6-79 Message composer for editing messages used by a test scenario; the *RRCConnectionReconfiguration* message is shown.

6.6 LTE terminal conformance testing and certification

Some references to the 3GPP conformance testing regime have already been made in previous chapters. An overview of the process and its contributors is given in Fig. 6-80.

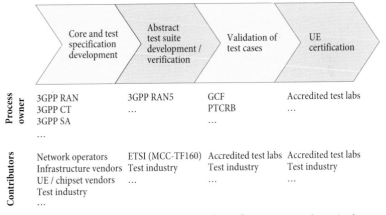

Fig. 6-80 LTE terminal conformance testing and certification process (overview).

3GPP defines conformance test cases for LTE FDD and TDD terminals based on the core specifications. In this process, the different 3GPP working groups work closely together (e.g. RAN = radio access network, CT = core network and terminals, SA = service & system aspects). Important conformance test specifications for LTE terminal testing are listed in the following:

I 3GPP TS 36.508 [Ref. 23]: E-UTRA and EPC; Common test environments for User Equipment (UE) conformance testing

I 3GPP TS 36.509 [Ref. 27]: E-UTRA and EPC; Special conformance testing functions for User Equipment (UE)

I 3GPP TS 36.521-1 [Ref. 22]: E-UTRA; User Equipment (UE) conformance specification; Radio transmission and reception; Part 1: Conformance Testing

I 3GPP TS 36.521-2 [Ref. 28]: E-UTRA; User Equipment (UE) conformance specification; Radio transmission and reception; Part 2: Implementation Conformance Statement (ICS)

I 3GPP TS 36.521-3 [Ref. 29]: E-UTRA; User Equipment (UE) conformance specification; Radio transmission and reception; Part 3: Radio Resource Management (RRM) conformance testing

I 3GPP TS 36.523-1 [Ref. 26]: E-UTRA and EPC; User Equipment (UE) conformance specification; Part 1: Protocol conformance specification

I 3GPP TS 36.523-2 [Ref. 30]: E-UTRA and EPC; User Equipment (UE) conformance specification; Part 2: Implementation Conformance Statement (ICS)

I 3GPP TS 36.523-3 [Ref. 31]: E-UTRA and EPC; User Equipment (UE) conformance specification; Part 3: Test Suites

Besides the test case descriptions themselves, the framework also specifies test environments, testing functions and the applicability of tests. The implementation conformance statement (ICS) specifications are intended to ensure that manufacturers provide information about the implementation of a product in a standardized manner.

For LTE signaling conformance test cases, an additional process step exists: The test cases as specified in prose in 3GPP TS 36.523-1 [Ref. 26] are provided as a complete test suite in the internationally standardized testing language Testing and Test Control Notation – Version 3 (TTCN-3). A special taskforce, the European Telecommunications Standards Institute, Mobile Competence Centre – Task Force 160 (ETSI

MCC-TF 160) is responsible for this step. These tests are then verified with real implementations. The focus in the conformance tests is on verification of compliance of terminals to the 3GPP LTE standard in order to ensure worldwide interoperability of the terminal within every mobile network.

Terminal certification for LTE is based on these 3GPP test specifications (plus additional ones for other test areas, e.g. for audio testing). Note that besides 3GPP, further specification development organizations (SDOs) define standards and test specifications that may be referenced by the certification organizations. The terminal certification process was already established for GSM and UMTS and has been adapted in a similar manner for LTE. It is recognized by the industry as a quality gateway for terminal acceptance in a mobile network and as a key contribution to ensure global interoperability. Certification organizations define certification criteria for terminals based on the conformance test cases. This process typically also includes prioritization of the high number of test cases in accordance with network operator requirements. The terminal must pass validated test cases implemented on registered test platforms in order to conform to these criteria. This part of the process is usually handled by accredited test labs. Work in certification organizations is based on a partnership between network operators, device manufacturers and the test industry and requires a close liaison with the standardization fora.

For LTE, terminal certification has started at the end of 2010.

6.7 Interference hunting, LTE network optimization and coverage measurements

Network operators face special testing challenges when planning and deploying LTE networks. Depending on the frequency band selected for LTE operation, different co-existence scenarios with other technologies deployed in adjacent bands must be considered. Furthermore, in many countries worldwide, LTE is deployed in frequency bands that were previously allocated to broadcast services (the so-called "digital dividend").

In every case, the network operator must ensure there are no potential sources of interference in the spectrum intended for LTE operation. **Spectrum clearing** is thus a major task that involves checking for leftover emitters that could cause interference problems. But even when the network is already installed, identification and location of interferers ("**interference hunting**") are still important since the interference situation can of course change over time and interferers may occur only irregularly. Portable receivers allow identification of unknown signals over a very wide bandwidth and are therefore a key component in interference hunting. Portable spectrum analyzers allow characterization of known signals. Note that these interferers do not necessarily originate in cellular or broadcast networks, but can come from any wireless source or even result from leakage from wired transmissions.

LTE base station locations and coverage areas must be carefully planned. Powerful network scanners (see Fig. 6-81) enable thorough analysis of the LTE air interface by measuring important LTE radio parameters and thus identifying coverage gaps or improperly configured base stations.

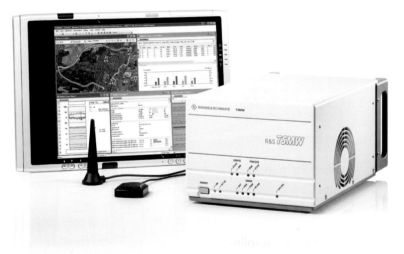

Fig. 6-81 The R&S®TSMW network scanner for LTE network deployment and optimization.

These instruments automatically scan for available LTE cells based on the synchronization signals. With their sensitivity well below the noise level, interfering signals from other base stations can be discovered. Such pilot pollution is a common source of connectivity problems such as call drops. As the network scanner captures every signal on the air interface, unknown cells can be identified over a wide frequency range.

Network scanners can be integrated into complete coverage measurement solutions to allow thorough analysis of the data captured during drive tests and comparison of the scanner data with the data from real terminals. This process provides important feedback on how to optimally set LTE radio parameters so as to get the most out of the new technology. A sample measurement including a map view is shown in Fig. 6-82. Within the map, the signal-to-interference/noise (SINR) ratio is displayed along the road that was driven while measuring with the network scanner. Plus, the connections to the strongest base stations as seen from a certain measurement location are indicated.

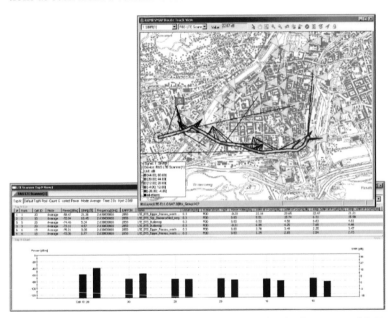

Fig. 6-82 The LTE top N view shows the N strongest signals with pilot power and SNR.

Another important capability for a network scanner is parallel measurement within different radio access technologies. This is an indispensable feature for the new LTE networks since they are expected to seamlessly integrate into the legacy 2G / 3G networks. System information from LTE or other technologies' cells can be demodulated to identify network information even for networks in neighboring countries.

7   Outlook

While previous chapters have focused largely on LTE as defined in 3GPP release 8 specifications, more enhancements are arriving in 3GPP releases 9 and 10. Moreover, the improvements planned for 3GPP release 10, also known as "LTE-Advanced", will take LTE to the next level and make it a true 4G technology. But let us first have a look at 3GPP release 9.

7.1   3GPP release 9

Due to the tight timeframes for finalizing the 3GPP release 8 specifications, some features were identified for movement to release 9. 3GPP release 9 therefore contains further increments and enhancements to LTE. This chapter highlights a few features that concern the radio access network.

7.1.1   Multimedia broadcast multicast services (MBMS) for LTE

MBMS will allow optimized transmission of the broadcast / point-to-multipoint type of services in LTE. MBMS has already been part of WCDMA / HSPA from 3GPP release 6 onwards and is now also available in LTE with some additional optimizations. MBMS for LTE is also referred to as enhanced MBMS (E-MBMS).

To support MBMS, LTE makes it possible to transmit multicast / broadcast data over a so-called single frequency network (MBSFN = multimedia broadcast multicast service single frequency network). All cells belonging to a so-called MBSFN area are coordinated for MBSFN transmission and transmit a time-synchronized common waveform for a given duration. This implies that the eNodeBs within an MBSFN area are synchronized. From the point of view of the terminal, this appears to be a single transmission as if originating from one large cell (with correspondingly large delay spread). The cyclic prefix is utilized to cover the difference in the propagation delays from the multiple cells. MBMS therefore uses an extended cyclic prefix.

Within one carrier, MBSFN transmissions are mixed with regular unicast / point-to-point data transmissions using time division multiplexing. The scheduling of MBSFN transmissions lies within the responsibility of the network.

Within the 3GPP release 8 specifications, some important features necessary for MBMS operation, particularly on the physical layer, were already defined. The full framework needed for MBMS operation, especially involving the higher layer and architectural aspects, is specified only from 3GPP release 9 onwards. The E-MBMS logical architecture with new logical network entities is shown in Fig. 7-1.

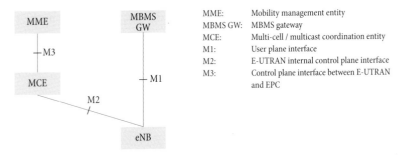

MME:	Mobility management entity
MBMS GW:	MBMS gateway
MCE:	Multi-cell / multicast coordination entity
M1:	User plane interface
M2:	E-UTRAN internal control plane interface
M3:	Control plane interface between E-UTRAN and EPC

Fig. 7-1   E-MBMS logical architecture.

Source: [3GPP TS 36.300 rel. 9, Ref. 32], reproduced by permission of 3GPP

MBMS user data is provided by the MBMS gateway (MBMS GW) to the eNodeB. The multi-cell / multicast coordination entity (MCE) handles admission control and decides on allocation of resources used by all eNodeBs in the MBSFN area. New interfaces M1-M3 are defined between the entities as shown in Fig. 7-1.

On the physical layer, MBMS has the following impact:
ı Another extended **cyclic prefix** configuration has been specified for MBMS usage in order to take into account the propagation delays of the multi-cell transmissions. This extended cyclic prefix has a length of 33.3 μs corresponding to 1024 samples and is based on a slot length of 3 OFDM symbols and a subcarrier spacing of $\Delta f = 7.5$ kHz.
ı Each MBSFN subframe is divided into an MBSFN region and a non-MBSFN region. The latter spans the first one or two OFDM symbols of a subframe and carries layer 1/2 control channels.
ı A **physical multicast channel (PMCH)** has been specified to carry MBMS user and control data. The PMCH can be transmitted only in

the MBSFN region of MBSFN subframes and carries the multicast channel (MCH) as the transport channel. Modulation and coding parameters for PMCH are configured by the higher layers.

I The MBSFN region of a subframe uses a special MBSFN reference signal structure.

Configuration of the MBMS services and related channels is performed by the higher layers. The new *SystemInformationBlockType13* contains the information required to acquire the MBMS control information associated with one or more MBSFN areas. MBMS user data is carried by the logical **multicast traffic channel (MTCH)** which is mapped onto the multicast channel (MCH) as a transport channel. Multiple MBMS services can be mapped onto the same MCH. For providing control and scheduling information about the MBMS services to the terminals, the logical **multicast control channel (MCCH)** is used, which is also mapped onto the MCH and can be multiplexed with the MTCH. The terminals are notified about changes in the MCCH information. This MCCH change notification is performed using DCI format 1C on the PDCCH, scrambled with a special M-RNTI identity.

For terminal testing, special MBMS reference channels and an LTE MBSFN channel model have been defined in 3GPP release 9.

7.1.2 Dual-layer beamforming

Dual-layer beamforming extends the release 8 concept of single-layer beamforming. Users with good channel conditions will be able to exploit transmission via two spatial layers, i.e. based on spatial multiplexing, thereby increasing their throughput. As with single-layer beamforming, **UE-specific reference signals** will be used, but additional patterns have been introduced from release 9 onwards in order to support dual-layer beamforming. Effectively, reference signal patterns for two additional antenna ports 7 and 8 have been defined in [36.211 rel. 9, Ref. 33]. Even multi-user transmissions are supported based on orthogonal reference signals on antenna ports 7 and 8, with each user having a rank-1 transmission. The network can configure whether the terminal is expected to report the **precoding matrix indicator (PMI)**.

A new transmission mode 8 has been introduced for dual-layer beamforming as an additional MIMO transmission mode (cf. chapter 5.5.2, page 54). It is mandatory for TDD terminals and optional for FDD terminals. A new DCI format 2B is used for transmission mode 8. It allows signaling of up to two transport blocks and the assignment of antenna port 7 or 8 in case only one transport block is transmitted.

The terminal performance tests for UE-specific reference signals stipulated by the specification 3GPP TS 36.521 [Ref. 22] have been enhanced in release 9 to take into account transmission mode 8. Performance of antenna ports 7 and 8 is tested for both single-layer and dual-layer spatial multiplexing.

7.1.3 RF requirements for multicarrier and multi-RAT base stations

Multi-carrier and multi-standard radio (MSR) base stations are a natural consequence of the multitude of cellular deployment scenarios, taking into account GSM/EDGE, WCDMA/HSPA, TD-SCDMA and LTE technologies as well as the different bandwidths of operation. An LTE-only ("single-RAT") base station can already support multiple carriers, each possibly providing a different bandwidth between 1.4 MHz and 20 MHz. The scenarios obviously become more complex if different carriers provide different radio access technologies.

A work item was therefore started for 3GPP release 9 in order to clarify which RF requirements these base stations have to support. This was not addressed or only partly addressed in previous base station specifications. A new specification TS 37.104 [Ref. 34] was developed which covers minimum RF requirements for multi-carrier and multi-standard base stations. E-UTRA, UTRA and GSM/EDGE standards are addressed. A corresponding conformance test specification TS 37.141 [Ref. 35] has been provided as well.

Per definition of [Ref. 34], an MSR base station is a
"Base station characterized by the ability of its receiver and transmitter to process two or more carriers in common active RF components simulta-

neously in a declared RF bandwidth, where at least one carrier is of a different RAT than the other carrier(s)."

Obviously, many RF requirements for a single-RAT base station also apply to an MSR base station. Thus, [Ref. 34] contains many references to the corresponding single-RAT specifications for the different technologies and by no means is intended to replace the existing single-RAT specifications.

Not all combinations of standards are supported in all operating bands. For defining the MSR base station requirements, [Ref. 34] therefore divides the operating bands into three band categories:

- Band category 1 (BC1): Bands for E-UTRA FDD and UTRA FDD operation
- Band category 2 (BC2): Bands for E-UTRA FDD, UTRA FDD and GSM/EDGE operation
- Band category 3 (BC3): Bands for E-UTRA TDD and UTRA TDD operation

7.1.4 Home eNodeB specification

A Home eNodeB (HeNB) is often also referred to as a femto base station or femto cell for LTE. The concept of Home eNodeB in 3GPP is based on the corresponding concept of Home NodeBs (HNB) for UMTS WCDMA/HSPA. Femto cells have already been commercially available for some years for different technologies including e.g. WCDMA/HSPA and WiMAX™. The prime objective of femto cells is to provide improved indoor coverage as well as attractive services and increased data rates in home environments. They are typically associated with uncoordinated and large-scale deployment, thus requiring specific thoughts on interference protection for the macro deployments.

For LTE, the initial features for the Home eNodeB specification have already been prepared in release 8. Release 9 brings further enhancements to the specification for both Home NodeBs and Home eNodeBs, but in particular includes the RF requirement specifications for FDD and TDD Home eNodeBs.

Similar to WCDMA/HSPA, the LTE base station specifications 3GPP TS 36.104 [Ref. 36] and 3GPP TS 36.141 [Ref. 37] have been enhanced where necessary to take into account HeNB-specific RF requirements. A home BS class has been introduced with dedicated BS output power requirements, including additional requirements for protecting E-UTRA and UTRA operation in adjacent channels. Furthermore, there are home BS specific requirements for other base station RF requirements as well in order to take into account the specific needs and challenges of this type of base station.

7.1.5 Self-organizing networks (SON)

The concept of self-organizing networks (SON) is fundamentally changing the way mobile networks are deployed and operated since it will automate many tasks that previously had to be performed manually. This is of crucial importance for LTE since the overall complexity of the networks is steadily increasing due to multi-technology environments, tight spectrum usage, advanced radio interface features and parameterization as well as the expected higher numbers of network elements especially due to Home eNodeB introduction. Another important aspect is that system operability is improved for multi-vendor environments, i.e. measurements and performance data from different vendors should be compatible. Self organizing networks are important for the network operator to save costs, both on the CAPEX and OPEX sides, and to efficiently manage the new generation of mobile networks and achieve successful LTE commercialization.

Work on SON was actually initiated in 3GPP release 8 and is still ongoing beyond release 9. SON particularly affects the operation and maintenance concepts as well as the architecture, e.g. how network elements exchange information with each other and which SON-related functions are located in which part of the network. SON comprises a wide variety of use cases: Typically, there is a distinction between self-configuration, self-optimization and self-healing functions. Self-configuration addresses the automatic recognition and configuration of a new base station in order to reduce the human intervention required in this process. A new base station will automatically set its basic configuration parameters, identify its neighbor base stations and establish neighbor relations to them. Self-optimization refers to the continuous optimization and fine-tuning of network operation, e.g. by adjusting neighbor cell lists or handover parameters. As an input to self-optimization, measurements from terminals and base stations are evaluated. Self-healing functions try to detect and correct faults, e.g. cell outages, in the network automatically.

7.2 LTE-Advanced

The International Telecommunication Union (ITU) has defined the requirements for 4G / IMT-Advanced technologies. The term "IMT-Advanced" refers to mobile systems whose capabilities go beyond those of the IMT 2000 framework of technology. Especially challenging are the data rate requirements: IMT-Advanced technologies must achieve 1 Gbps peak downlink data rate in low mobility scenarios and 100 Mbps in high mobility scenarios. This can only be achieved with bandwidth extensions up to 100 MHz operating bandwidth. Throughout 2009, 3GPP has worked on a feasibility study [Ref. 38] identifying a number of LTE improvements in order to meet these IMT-Advanced requirements. Based on the ITU requirements, 3GPP created a technical report summarizing LTE-Advanced requirements in 3GPP TR 36.913 [Ref. 39]. In September 2009, the 3GPP partners made a formal submission to the ITU proposing that LTE release 10 and beyond (LTE-Advanced) should be evaluated as candidate for IMT-Advanced. Note that LTE-Advanced is not the only technology candidate for IMT-Advanced. WiMAX™ 802.16m has also been proposed to the ITU. In the following, a short overview is provided of the new technology components in LTE-Advanced.

7.2.1 Band aggregation

LTE-Advanced needs to operate in spectrum allocations wider than the 20 MHz specified in LTE Release 8. This can be achieved either by contiguous spectrum allocation (Fig. 7-2) or by non-contiguous spectrum allocation (Fig. 7-3). In both cases, multiple component carriers are bundled to support wider transmission bandwidths up to 100 MHz.

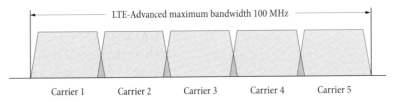

Fig. 7-2 Aggregation of contiguous component carriers.

Fig. 7-3 Aggregation of non-contiguous component carriers.

Initial LTE-Advanced (3GPP Release 10) deployments will likely be limited to the use of a maximum of two component carriers, i.e. the maximum DL/UL bandwidth will be 40 MHz for FDD. This will not preclude a higher number of aggregated carriers to be specified in 3GPP Release 11 and / or higher.

In order to support legacy LTE Release 8 terminals, it must be possible for each of the component carriers to be configured as an LTE Release 8 carrier. However, not all component carriers may necessarily be compatible with LTE Release 8.

Band aggregation is available for the downlink and uplink. Many different scenarios have been investigated in 3GPP, considering the different frequency bands and different contiguous or non-contiguous deployment scenarios.

7.2.2 Enhanced MIMO

As described in 5.5.2, page 54, LTE release 8 already supports a wide range of MIMO schemes and configuration options. These are further enhanced by LTE-Advanced. LTE-Advanced extends the MIMO capabilities of LTE Release 8 to support eight downlink antennas at the base station and four uplink antennas at the terminal. In the uplink direction, the same principles as defined in LTE release 8 downlink are re-used whereas in the downlink direction the existing scheme is simply extended. In the case of downlink spatial multiplexing using eight antennas, up to two code words / transport blocks can be transmitted to one terminal per subframe per component carrier. In the uplink of LTE-Advanced, the terminal may transmit up to two code words / transport blocks, with each transport block having its own modulation and coding scheme. As in the downlink, different codebooks with precoding matrices are defined depending on the number of available transmit antennas and transmission layers.

7.2.3 Enhanced uplink transmission scheme

The uplink transmission scheme for LTE-Advanced uses SC-FDMA as in LTE release 8. However, in contrast to LTE release 8, simultaneous PUCCH / PUSCH transmission is possible in the uplink direction, with PUCCH being used for uplink control information and PUSCH for user data. Furthermore, while LTE release 8 only allows localized SC-FDMA transmission with contiguously allocated resource blocks, LTE-Advanced does not have this restriction. Clusters of subcarriers can be allocated in order to support uplink frequency selective scheduling for optimized link performance.

7.2.4 Coordinated multiple point transmission and reception (CoMP)

Coordinated multi-point (CoMP) transmission / reception is considered as a tool to improve cell-edge throughput and increase system throughput for LTE-Advanced.

In a cellular deployment and specifically in cases where frequencies are reused in each cell, other-cell interference traditionally degrades the system capacity. The objective of CoMP is to turn the other-cell interference into a useful signal specifically at the cell border. This requires support for joint processing of received signals at multiple geographically separated points and also dynamic coordination in the scheduling / transmission, including joint transmission, from multiple geographically separate points as illustrated in Fig. 7-4.

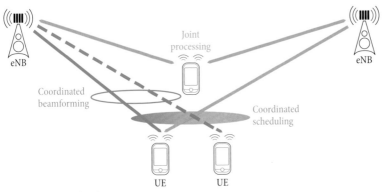

Fig. 7-4   Principle of CoMP.

In the downlink direction, one can distinguish between joint processing (JP) and coordinated scheduling (CS) / coordinated beamforming (CB). In the joint processing case, transmission data to a single terminal is available at each transmission point, i.e. at multiple base stations. Joint transmission is characterized either by simultaneous transmission of the user data to the terminal from multiple base stations, or – in the dynamic cell selection case – data is transmitted from one base station at a time only. For coordinated scheduling / beamforming, data is always transmitted from one base station only; however, user scheduling / beamforming decisions are made based on coordination among cells.

In the CoMP uplink (reception) direction, multi-point reception implies coordination among multiple base stations. Uplink CoMP reception involves joint reception (JR) of the transmitted signal at multiple reception points and / or coordinated scheduling (CS) decisions among cells to control interference.

Different approaches to the network architecture are possible. In a centralized approach, one central unit receives all relevant feedback data and pre-computes all waveforms which are sent to remote base stations for over-the-air transmission. In consequence, high-capacity backhaul transmission is required for fulfilling high latency requirements. In a distributed cooperation approach, base stations exchange data via the X2 interface in smaller clusters of grouped base stations, whereas each base station has to compute the waveforms. In both cases, the solution relies on channel feedback information either received via a feedback channel from the terminal (FDD) or by exploiting channel reciprocity (TDD).

7.2.5 Relaying

Relaying was introduced in LTE-Advanced in order to increase coverage and capacity of the network. In relaying, the terminal(s) communicates with the relay which in turn communicates with a donor eNodeB. The relay node is wirelessly connected to the donor cell of a donor eNodeB via the so-called Un interface, and terminals connect to the relay station via the well-known Uu interface as shown in Fig. 7-5. The transmission over Un and Uu can occur over the same frequency band (in-band relaying) or on different frequency bands (out-of-band relaying). Transmissions to and from the relay station on the same frequency resource typically must be time-multiplexed in order to avoid blocking of the relay receiver.

The donor eNodeB may, in addition to serving one or several relays, also communicate with non-relayed terminals directly as was the case in 3GPP release 8.

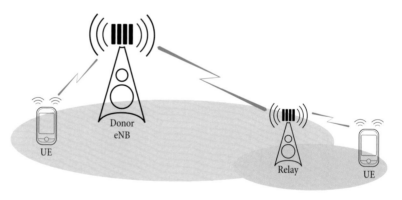

Fig. 7-5 Relaying

Depending on the degree of intelligence and functionality, different relay classes exist. The simplest implementation is a so-called layer 1 relay station which basically functions as a repeater, thereby merely receiving the donor eNodeB signal and amplifying it into its own coverage area. A layer 2 relay station contains medium access control (MAC) layer functionality. It is able to decode received signals and reencode them for transmission in order to achieve higher link quality in the relay cell area. The performance gain comes at the expense of higher complexity (cost) of the relay and also adds delay to the communication link. A layer 3 relay station includes functionality such as mobility management, session setup and handover and therefore serves as a full-service (sub-) eNodeB. This adds more complexity to the implementation of such a relay node and the delay budget is further increased. Furthermore, relay stations can be distinguished in terms of whether they transmit their own cell identity (type 1 relay stations) and their own synchronization and reference signals or not (type 2 relay stations). Type 1 relay stations basically appear to the terminal as an eNodeB. In contrast, transmissions from type 2 relay stations cannot be distinguished by the terminal from the donor eNodeB's transmission. This allows transmission of control information from the eNodeB and data from the type 2 relay station; see Fig. 7-6.

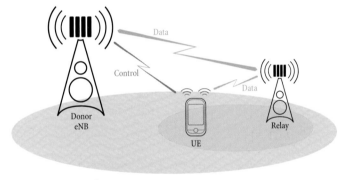

Fig. 7-6   Type 2 relay station.

8   Appendices

8.1   Current Rohde&Schwarz range of T&M equipment for LTE

Signal generation
The whole world of wireless communications

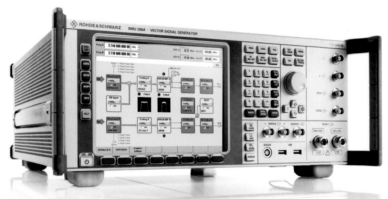

Fig. 8-1   R&S®SMU200A vector signal generator.

The R&S®SMU200A vector signal generator has been tailored for the wireless digital communications age. It meets all requirements encountered during research, development and production of state-of-the-art communications systems. The R&S®SMU200A not only combines up to two independent signal generators (two baseband and RF sections) in one cabinet, it also offers unrivaled RF and baseband characteristics – including a 40-path fading simulator. The instrument can be fitted with a wide range of options to cover all of today's important digital standards and to provide function and performance enhancements such as MIMO fading or phase coherence. The wide scope of LTE features allows virtually any parameter or behavior of interest to be adjusted, including the OFDMA and SC-FDMA physical layer modes and the FDD and TDD duplex modes. Base station conformance is tested in line with 3GPP TS 36.141. HARQ feedback and timing adjustment commands are processed in realtime. For pure baseband applications such as found in chip development, the R&S®AMU200A baseband signal generator and fading generator can be used. When configured as a baseband fading simulator, the R&S®AMU200A, together with the R&S®CMW500 wideband radio communication tester, provides an ideal combination for fading tests with signaling

Signal generation
Complex signals out of the box

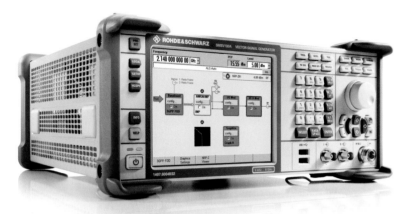

Fig. 8-2   R&S®SMBV100A signal generator.

At a mid-range price, the R&S®SMBV100A signal generator provides the measuring convenience of high end models such as the
R&S®SMU200A. Even complex signals can be defined directly in
the instrument – without a PC. An intuitive graphical user interface
together with the optional baseband generator and the high-quality
I/Q modulator make it easy to generate signals in line with all important
wireless communications standards, including LTE, UMTS, WiMAX™
and WLAN. The R&S®SMBV100A offers even more: For applications that need very wide broadband modulation, such as UWB, the
R&S®SMBV100A can modulate signals from an external I/Q source up
to an RF bandwidth of 528 MHz. Another highlight in its class: The
high output power of up to +24 dBm eliminates the need for external
amplifiers in power attenuation test setups.

Power measurement
Unmatched precision and versatility

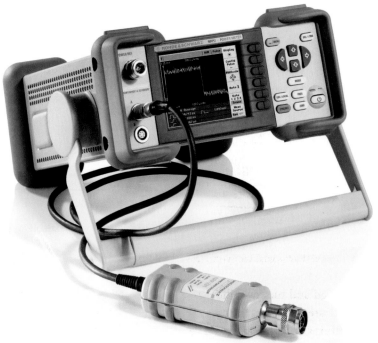

Fig. 8-3   R&S®NRP2 base unit with sensor.

Radiocommunications standards such as 3GPP FDD, CDMA2000® or 3GPP LTE exhibit very different power profiles depending on their channel utilization. Assessing these power profiles is a routine job with the sensors of the R&S®NRP family. This is true no matter whether you need to accurately measure the average power, peak power or peak-to-average ratio in the time domain or if you need fast statistical analysis to precisely determine the amplitude distribution. The R&S®NRP family comprises a wide selection of sensors based on either diode, diode multipath or thermal technology, for frequencies up to 67 GHz and powers up to 30 W. They can be operated directly from a PC, from an R&S®NRP2 base unit or from many Rohde&Schwarz instruments.

When only the best will do:
R&S®FSW signal and spectrum analyzer

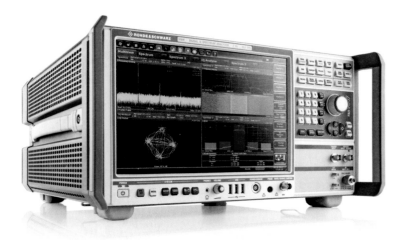

Fig. 8-4   R&S®FSW signal and spectrum analyzer.

The design and the capabilities of the R&S®FSW signal and spectrum analyzer are unique on the market. Developed for the most demanding applications in aerospace and defense as well as for the wideband communications systems of the future, its specifications outclass all other solutions offered to date. 160 MHz analysis bandwidth, phase noise 10 dB to 20 dB better than comparable instruments, noise level up to –173 dBm (1 Hz), a measurement uncertainty of only 0.4 dB to 8 GHz and up to 1000 sweeps per second are benchmark figures that make this analyzer one of a kind. However, just as remarkable are the innovations in measurement and usability implemented on the R&S®FSW that will revolutionize the operation of this kind of instrument. For example, the fast measurement and processing speeds allow multiple analyses to be performed in parallel and the results to be displayed together on the large touchscreen (MultiView, see photo). The multistandard radio analyzer integrated into the R&S®FSW goes even one step further: Within the analysis bandwidth of 160 MHz, signals based on different (mobile) radio technologies can be measured simultaneously in realtime and then compared to ascertain their effects on each other. The R&S®FSW offers a host of exceptional features, including amazingly simple operation using softtools, security functionality permitting use in classified environments, and the system-level ability to operate up to four power sensors in parallel, to name just a few.

Signal and spectrum analysis
For the most demanding applications

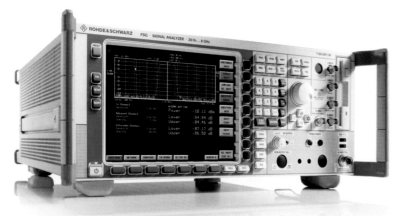

Fig. 8-5   R&S®FSQ signal analyzer.

The R&S®FSQ signal analyzer was specially designed to analyze the physical parameters and modulation characteristics of digital wireless communications systems. A wide frequency range (models with an upper limit of 3.6 GHz to 40 GHz), 120 MHz analysis bandwidth, analog and digital baseband inputs as well as RF ports, and outstanding RF characteristics make the R&S®FSQ a universal analysis tool in the development lab or in production. The excellent hardware characteristics are utilized by numerous software options, e.g. for general, standard-independent vector signal analysis and also for all standard cellular and non-cellular wireless technologies such as LTE, UMTS, GSM and WLAN.

Signal and spectrum analysis
The benchmark for speed and convenience

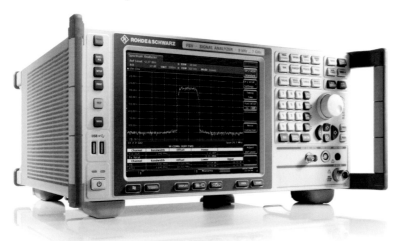

Fig. 8-6   R&S®FSV signal and spectrum analyzer.

The R&S®FSV signal and spectrum analyzer not only boasts top features such as a 40 MHz analysis bandwidth and a level measurement uncertainty of only 0.4 dB to 7 GHz, it also exhibits an impressive speed of up to 1000 sweeps per second, allowing even CPU-intensive measurement to be performed quickly and without interruption. In seconds, thousands of individual measurements can be averaged, statistical functions such as CCDF can be performed, or the analysis software can be changed. Operations such as marker positioning, which up to now have been cumbersome, are simplified by the touchscreen display. A wide range of software options allow specific analysis of signals for diverse wireless network and wireless personal area network standards. The LTE option includes functions for measuring the modulation type and quality, MIMO, spectrum, and power.

Installation and service
Versatility to go

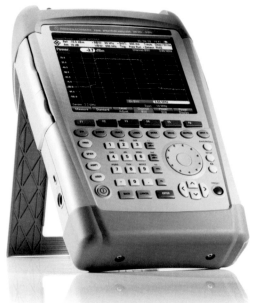

Fig. 8-7   R&S®FSH 8 handheld spectrum analyzer.

The R&S®FSH 4 / FSH 8 spectrum analyzer provides an RF service technician or installation and maintenance team with all the analysis functions they need to solve everyday measurement tasks, for example when installing antennas or wireless communications base stations. The robust, splash-proof analyzer covers spectrum analysis, network analysis, power measurements, cable and antenna testing, and modulation analysis. LTE transmitter measurements are made possible by simply activating the appropriate software option. Measurements can then be performed in the LTE FDD and LTE TDD mode – at a bandwidth of 20 MHz, as specified in the standard. The R&S®FSH 4 / FSH 8 also supports measurements on LTE MIMO signals. This option measures the power and EVM of the physical channels, and lists them separately. This allows the user to detect transmitter impairments that are difficult to recognize in the spectrum, such as clipping or intermodulation.

Radiocommunications testing
All wireless standards under control

Fig. 8-8   R&S®CMW 500 wideband radio communication tester.

The R&S®CMW 500 wideband radio communication tester is an all-in-one, multi-technology test platform for wireless devices. Chipset and wireless device manufacturers as well as network operators benefit from its unrivaled flexibility, speed and scope of functions. Practically all wireless standards that might be found in a mobile device are covered – from 2G and 3G mobile radio to non-cellular standards such as WLAN, GPS and Bluetooth®, to broadcasting technologies such as DVB-T or FM stereo. LTE is fully represented by appropriate test functions for RF generation and analysis, network emulation ("call box" function), protocol testing and end-to-end application testing. But the R&S®CMW 500 is not only multi-technology, it is also multi-role. Manufacturers can configure the platform for ultra-high-speed non-signaling production tests whereas protocol and application developers can deeply manipulate the "gearbox" of the diverse standards, adapting signaling functions and the upper communications layers according to their needs.

RF tests

Consistent testing from R&D to conformance

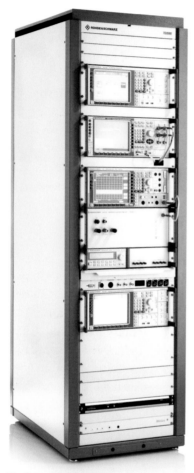

The R&S®TS 8980 family of test systems offers industry's most complete coverage of applications in WCDMA and LTE testing. The R&S®TS 8980 is used by all of the leading test houses as well as first-rate chipset and UE manufacturers plus major network operators. UTRA and E-UTRA conformance tests in line with GCF and PTCRB are complemented by acceptance test packages as defined by many network operators. The R&S CONTEST graphical user interface allows control over test case execution and automation of DUT, climatic chamber, DC supply and external devices. The GUI offers functions for DUT management and result reporting as well as internal and external database control for result handling and storage. Modular, upgradeable hardware and software configurations are available, ranging from a benchtop combination of R&D instruments to fully rack-integrated conformance test systems.

Fig. 8-9   R&S®TS 8980 RF conformance test system.

RF tests for LTE and WCDMA may be combined with RRM conformance and performance analysis. Location-based service test plans round out the range of applications.

OTA measurements
A close look at the air interface

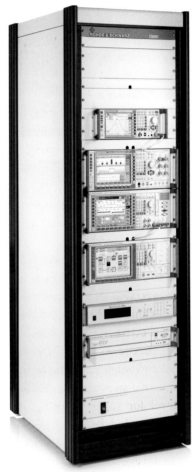

Over-the-air (OTA) measurements help operators increase the efficiency of their networks. The R&S®TS8991 OTA performance test system was especially designed to perform these measurements. It characterizes the three-dimensional power distribution and sensitivity of wireless devices, i.e. its over-the-air performance, expressed by parameters such as total radiated power (TRP) and total isotropic sensitivity (TIS). In addition, radiation pattern measurements on antennas are possible. The R&S®TS8991 can be ordered in tailored versions for many mobile radio standards. The LTE version provides a cost-effective two-channel measurement method for verifying MIMO devices.

Fig. 8-10 R&S®TS8991 OTA performance test system.

Performance quality analysis
Bringing real world conditions to the lab

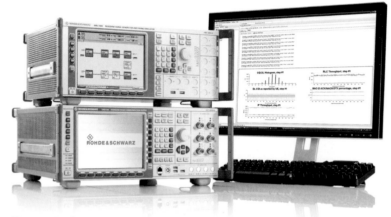

Fig. 8-11 Performance quality analysis solution.

In normal use, a mobile phone is constantly experiencing changing reception conditions as it moves to the extremities of a cell, during handover between technologies, or simply due to interference affecting a signal. These are real-world factors that mobile radio standards largely do not take into consideration. For network operators, however, these are critical factors. They can test such real-world conditions using a performance quality analysis system from Rohde & Schwarz which facilitates automated end-to-end tests between the mobile device and a base station.

Drive tests
Investigate what's out there

Fig. 8-12 R&S®TSMW universal radio network analyzer

The R&S®TSMW universal radio network analyzer is a high-end drive test platform for optimizing all conventional wireless communications networks. Two highly sensitive RF paths for any input frequency from 30 MHz to 6 GHz with a bandwidth of 20 MHz each are combined with a software-defined architecture to offer unsurpassed performance while providing maximum flexibility and operational readiness. The R&S®TSMW is the only scanner capable of simultaneously measuring the parameters of six mobile radio standards from all three ITU regions worldwide, including LTE. In combination with the powerful R&S®ROMES4 drive test software, all essential tasks involved in coverage measurement, interference identification and QoS measurement can be carried out efficiently.

8.2 References

Ref. 1   3GPP TSG RAN Study Item Description Sheet After Meeting #41, Concluded SIs, http://www.3gpp.org/ftp/tsg_ran/TSG_RAN/Work_Item_sheets/

Ref. 2   3GPP TR 25.913; Requirements for E-UTRA and E-UTRAN (Release 7), V7.3.0 (2006-03)

Ref. 3   3GPP TS 25.401; UTRAN overall description (Release 99), V3.10.0 (2002-06)

Ref. 4   3GPP TS 36.300; E-UTRA and E-UTRAN; Overall description; Stage 2 (Release 8), V8.12.0 (2010-03)

Ref. 5   3GPP TS 23.401; General Packet Radio Service (GPRS) enhancements for Evolved Universal Terrestrial Radio Access Network (E-UTRAN) access (Release 8), V8.9.0 (2010-03)

Ref. 6   3GPP TS 36.101; User Equipment (UE) radio transmission and reception (Release 9), V9.3.0 (2010-03)

Ref. 7   3GPP TS 36.211; Physical Channels and Modulation (Release 8), V8.9.0 (2010-03)

Ref. 8   Fuqin Xiong, Digital Modulation Techniques, Second Edition, ARTECH HOUSE, INC., 2006, ISBN 1-58053-863-0

Ref. 9   3GPP TR 25.892; Feasibility Study for Orthogonal Frequency Division Multiplexing (OFDM) for UTRAN enhancement (Release 6), V6.0.0 (2004-06)

Ref. 10   3GPP TS 36.101; User Equipment (UE) radio transmission and reception (Release 8), V8.9.0 (2010-03)

Ref. 11   Hyung G. Myung, David J. Goodman, Single Carrier FDMA: A New Air Interface for Long Term Evolution, Wiley, 2008, ISBN 978-0-470-72449-1

Ref. 12   3GPP TS 36.212; Multiplexing and Channel Coding (Release 8), V8.8.0 (2009-12)

Ref. 13   Chu, D.C., "Polyphase codes with good periodic correlation properties", IEEE Transactions Information Theory, vol. 18, pp. 531 to 532, July 1972

Ref. 14   S.M. Alamouti (October 1998). "A simple transmit diversity technique for wireless communications", IEEE Journal on Selected Areas in Communications, Vol. 16., No. 8

Ref. 15   3GPP TS 36.213; Physical Layer Procedures (Release 8), V8.8.0 (2009-09)

Ref. 16   3GPP TS 36.321; Medium Access Control (MAC) protocol specification (Release 8), V8.8.0 (2009-12)

Ref. 17 LTE resource allocation tool, http://www2.rohde-schwarz. com/en/technologies/cellular_standards/LTE/applications/article-TOOL__LTE_Resource_Allocation. html?cal_time=1226358967

Ref. 18 3GPP TS 36.331; Radio Resource Control (RRC) protocol specification (Release 8), V8.9.0 (2010-03)

Ref. 19 3GPP TS 36.306; User Equipment (UE) radio access capabilities (Release 8), V8.6.0 (2010-03)

Ref. 20 http://www.mipi.org/digrf.shtml

Ref. 21 http://www.cpri.info/

Ref. 22 3GPP TS 36.521-1; User Equipment (UE) conformance specification; Radio transmission and reception; Part 1: Conformance testing (Release 8), V8.5.0 (2010-03)

Ref. 23 3GPP TS 36.508; Common test environments for User Equipment (UE) conformance testing (Release 8), V8.5.0 (2010-03)

Ref. 24 3GPP TS 36.141; Base Station (BS) conformance testing (Release 8), V8.6.0 (2010-03)

Ref. 25 3GPP TS 36.104; Base Station (BS) radio transmission and reception (Release 8), V8.9.0 (2010-03)

Ref. 26 3GPP TS 36.523-1; User Equipment (UE) conformance specification; Part 1: Protocol conformance specification (Release 8), V8.5.0 (2010-03)

Ref. 27 3GPP TS 36.509; Special conformance testing functions for User Equipment (UE) (Release 8), V8.5.0 (2010-03)

Ref. 28 3GPP TS 36.521-2; User Equipment (UE) conformance specification; Radio transmission and reception; Part 2: Implementation Conformance Statement (ICS) (Release 8), V8.4.0 (2010-03)

Ref. 29 3GPP TS 36.521-3; User Equipment (UE) conformance specification; Radio transmission and reception; Part 3: Radio Resource Management (RRM) conformance testing (Release 8), V8.3.0 (2010-03)

Ref. 30 3GPP TS 36.523-2; User Equipment (UE) conformance specification; Part 2: Implementation Conformance Statement (ICS) proforma specification (Release 8), V8.5.0 (2010-03)

Ref. 31 3GPP TS 36.523-3; User Equipment (UE) conformance specification; Part 3: Test suites (Release 8), V8.2.0 (2010-03)

Ref. 32 3GPP TS 36.300; E-UTRA and E-UTRAN; Overall description; Stage 2 (Release 9), V9.3.0 (2010-03)

Ref. 33   3GPP TS 36.211; Physical Channels and Modulation (Release 9), V9.1.0 (2010-03)

Ref. 34   3GPP TS 37.104; E-UTRA, UTRAN and GSM/EDGE; Multi-Standard Radio (MSR) Base Station (BS) radio transmission and reception (Release 9), V9.1.0 (2010-03)

Ref. 35   3GPP TS 37.141; E-UTRA, UTRAN and GSM/EDGE; Multi-Standard Radio (MSR) Base Station (BS) conformance testing (Release 9), V0.3.0 (R4-100975, Ericsson, RAN WG4#54)

Ref. 36   3GPP TS 36.104; Base Station (BS) radio transmission and reception (Release 9), V9.3.0 (2010-03)

Ref. 37   3GPP TS 36.141; Base Station (BS) conformance testing (Release 9), V9.3.0 (2010-03)

Ref. 38   3GPP TR 36.912; Feasibility Study for Further Advancements for E-UTRA (LTE-Advanced) (Release 9), V9.2.0 (2010-03)

Ref. 39   3GPP TR 36.913; Requirements for further advancements for Evolved Universal Terrestrial Radio Access (E-UTRA) (LTE-Advanced) (Release 8), V9.0.0 (2009-12)

Ref. 40   3GPP TS 36.101; User Equipment (UE) radio transmission and reception (Release 10), V 10.4.0 (2011-09)

8.3 Abbreviations

1xRTT	1x Radio Transmission Technology
3GPP	3rd Generation Partnership Project
ACK	Acknowledgment
ACLR	Adjacent Channel Leakage Ratio
ACS	Adjacent Channel Selectivity
ARQ	Automatic Repeat Request
AS	Access Stratum
AWGN	Additive White Gaussian Noise
BC	Band Category
BCCH	Broadcast Control Channel
BCH	Broadcast Channel
BLER	Block Error Rate
BPSK	Binary Phase Shift Keying
BS	Base Station
CAPEX	Capital Expenditures
CAZAC	Constant Amplitude Zero Auto-Correlation
CB	Coordinated Beamforming
CCCH	Common Control Channel
CCE	Control Channel Element
CCO	Cell Change Order
CDMA	Code Division Multiple Access
CFI	Control Format Indicator
CoMP	Coordinated Multiple Point Transmission and Reception
CP	Cyclic Prefix
C-plane	Control Plane
CQI	Channel Quality Indicator
CRC	Cyclic Redundancy Check
C-RNTI	Cell Radio Network Temporary Identifier
CS	Circuit-Switched or Coordinated Scheduling (depending on context)
CW	Continuous Wave
DAI	Downlink Assignment Index
DCCH	Dedicated Control Channel
DCI	Downlink Control Information
DFT	Discrete Fourier Transform
DL	Downlink
DL-SCH	Downlink Shared Channel

DRS	Demodulation Reference Signal
DRX	Discontinuous Reception
DTCH	Dedicated Traffic Channel
DTX	Discontinuous Transmission
DUT	Device under Test
DwPTS	Downlink Pilot Timeslot
EDGE	Enhanced Data Rates for GSM Evolution
eNB	E-UTRAN NodeB
EPA	Extended Pedestrian
EPC	Evolved Packet Core
EPRE	Energy per Resource Element
EPS	Evolved Packet System
E-RAB	E-UTRAN Radio Access Bearer
E-TM	E-UTRA Test Model
ETU	Extended Typical Urban
ETWS	Earthquake and Tsunami Warning System
E-UTRA	Evolved Universal Terrestrial Radio Access
E-UTRAN	Evolved Universal Terrestrial Radio Access Network
EVA	Extended Vehicular
EVM	Error Vector Magnitude
FDD	Frequency Division Duplex
FFT	Fast Fourier Transform
FRC	Fixed Reference Channel
FSTD	Frequency-Switched Transmit Diversity
GBR	Guaranteed Bit Rate
GERAN	GSM EDGE Radio Access Network
GP	Guard Period
GPRS	General Packet Radio Service
GSM	Global System for Mobile Communications
GTP	GPRS Tunneling Protocol
HARQ	Hybrid Automatic Repeat Request
HI	HARQ Indicator
HeNB	Home eNodeB
HNB	Home NodeB
HO	Handover
HRPD	High Rate Packet Data
HSDPA	High Speed Downlink Packet Access
HSUPA	High Speed Uplink Packet Access
HSPA	High Speed Packet Access
HST	High Speed Train

ICS	Implementation Conformance Statement
ID	Identity
IDFT	Inverse Discrete Fourier Transform
IMT	International Mobile Telecommunications
IP	Internet Protocol
ITU	International Telecommunication Union
JP	Joint Processing
JR	Joint Reception
L1	Layer 1
L2	Layer 2
L3	Layer 3
LTE	Long Term Evolution
MAC	Medium Access Control
MBMS	Multimedia Broadcast Multicast Service
MBSFN	Multimedia Broadcast Multicast Service Single Frequency Network
MCCH	Multicast Control Channel
MCE	Multicell/Multicast Coordination Entity
MCH	Multicast Channel
MC-WCDMA	Multicarrier Wideband Code Division Multiple Access
MIMO	Multiple Input Multiple Output
MME	Mobility Management Entity
MSR	Multistandard Radio
MTCH	Multicast Traffic Channel
MU-MIMO	Multi-User MIMO
NACK	Negative Acknowledgment
NAS	Non-Access Stratum
OCNG	OFDMA Channel Noise Generator
OFDM	Orthogonal Frequency Division Multiplexing
OFDMA	Orthogonal Frequency Division Multiple Access
OPEX	Operational Expenditures
PAPR	Peak-to-Average Power Ratio
PBCH	Physical Broadcast Channel
PCCH	Paging Control Channel
PCFICH	Physical Control Format Indicator Channel
PCH	Paging Channel
PDCCH	Physical Downlink Control Channel
PDCP	Packet Data Convergence Protocol
PDSCH	Physical Downlink Shared Channel
PDU	Protocol Data Unit

P-GW	Packet Data Network Gateway
PHICH	Physical Hybrid ARQ Indicator Channel
PHY	Physical Layer
PMCH	Physical Multicast Channel
PRB	Physical Resource Block
PMI	Precoding Matrix Indicator
PRACH	Physical Random Access Channel
P-RNTI	Paging Radio Network Temporary Identifier
PS	Packet-Switched
PUCCH	Physical Uplink Control Channel
PUSCH	Physical Uplink Shared Channel
QAM	Quadrature Amplitude Modulation
QoS	Quality of Service
QPSK	Quadrature Phase Shift Keying
RACH	Random Access Channel
RA-RNTI	Random Access Radio Network Temporary Identifier
RAT	Radio Access Technology
RB	Radio Bearer or Resource Block (depending on context)
RBG	Resource Block Group
REG	Resource Element Group
RF	Radio Frequency
RI	Rank Indicator
RIV	Resource Indication Value
RLC	Radio Link Control
RNC	Radio Network Controller
RNTI	Radio Network Temporary Identifier
ROHC	Robust Header Compression
RRC	Radio Resource Control
RRM	Radio Resource Management
RS	Reference Signal
RU	Resource Unit
S1	Interface between eNB and EPC
S1-AP	S1 Application Protocol
SAE	System Architecture Evolution
SC-FDMA	Single-Carrier Frequency Division Multiple Access
SCH	Synchronization Channel
SCTP	Stream Control Transmission Protocol
SDMA	Spatial Division Multiple Access
SDO	Specification Development Organization

SDU	Service Data Unit
SEM	Spectrum Emission Mask
SFBC	Space-Frequency Block Coding
SIB	System Information Block
SI-RNTI	System Information Radio Network Temporary Identifier
SISO	Single Input Single Output
S-GW	Serving Gateway
SN	Sequence Number
SON	Self-Organizing Networks
SPS	Semi-Persistent Scheduling
SR	Scheduling Request
SRB	Signaling Radio Bearer
SRS	Sounding Reference Signal
TA	Timing Advance
TDD	Time Division Duplex
TD-SCDMA	Time Division Synchronous Code Division Multiple Access
TPC	Transmit Power Control
TS	Technical Specification
TTCN-3	Testing and Test Control Notation – Version 3
TTI	Transmission Time Interval
UCI	Uplink Control Information
UDP	User Datagram Protocol
UE	User Equipment
UL	Uplink
UL-SCH	Uplink Shared Channel
UMTS	Universal Mobile Telecommunications System
UPE	User Plane Entity
U-plane	User Plane
UpPTS	Uplink Pilot Timeslot
VoIP	Voice over IP
WCDMA	Wideband Code Division Multiple Access
WiMAX™	Worldwide Interoperability for Microwave Access
WLAN	Wireless Local Area Network
X2	Interface between eNBs
ZC	Zadoff-Chu

8.4 Index

M

N

O

215